P · O ·

BODY
FACTS

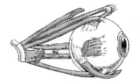

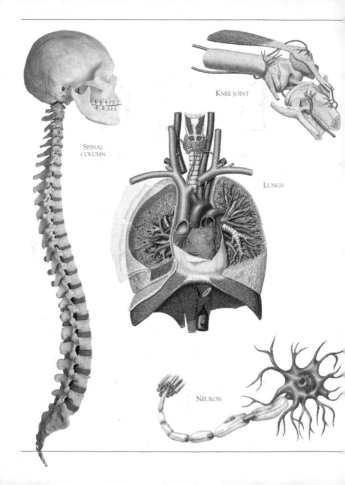

SPINAL
COLUMN

KNEE JOINT

LUNGS

NEURON

P·O·C·K·E·T·S

BODY
FACTS

Written by
DR SARAH BREWER

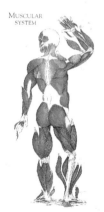

MUSCULAR
SYSTEM

SKULL

LYMPHATIC
SYSTEM

DORLING KINDERSLEY
London • New York • Stuttgart

A DORLING KINDERSLEY BOOK

Project editor	Caroline Brooke
Designer	Kate Eagar
Senior editor	Alastair Dougall
Senior art editor	Sarah Crouch
Picture research	Sam Ruston
Production	Josie Alabaster
	Katie Holmes

First published in Great Britain in 1996
by Dorling Kindersley Limited
9 Henrietta Street, Covent Garden, London WC2E 8PS

A CIP catalogue record for this book is available from
the British Library

ISBN 0 7513 5450 3

Colour reproduction by Colourscan, Singapore
Printed and bound in Italy by L.E.G.O.

CONTENTS

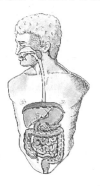

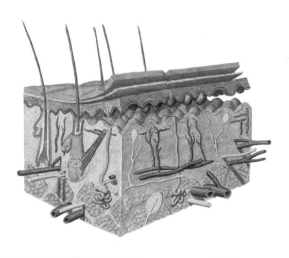

HOW TO USE THIS BOOK

These pages show you how to use *Pockets: Body Facts*.
The book is divided into six sections covering
different aspects of the human body, and there is
a reference section at the end. Each new section
begins with a contents page.

HEADING
This describes the subject of the
page. If a subject continues over
more than one page, the same
subject heading applies.

INTRODUCTION
The opening paragraph
provides an overview of the
subject and introduces you to
a number of key facts.

Heading   Introduction

Corner coding

Annotation

Caption

Label

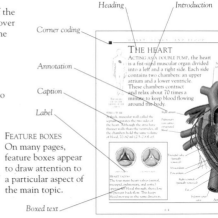

HEART, VEINS, AND BLOOD

THE HEART
ACTING AS A DOUBLE PUMP, the heart
is a fist-sized muscular organ divided
into a left and right side. Each side
contains two chambers: an upper
atrium and a lower ventricle.
These chambers contract
and relax about 70 times a
minute to keep blood flowing
around the body.

Heart valves
The four heart valves (mitral,
tricuspid, pulmonary, and aortic)
open to let blood through, then close
to prevent back flow. This keeps
blood moving in the same direction.

CORNER CODING	FEATURE BOXES
The page corners in the central sections are colour-coded to remind you which section you are in.	On many pages, feature boxes appear to draw attention to a particular aspect of the main topic.

■ BODY STRUCTURES

■ BRAIN AND
NERVOUS SYSTEM

■ HEART, BLOOD,
AND LUNGS

■ DIGESTION
AND EXCRETION

☐ REPRODUCTION

Boxed text

LABELS
Some pictures have
labels. These give extra
information or identify
a picture if it is not
immediately obvious
from the text.

CAPTIONS
Each illustration,
whether an artwork,
a photograph,
or a diagram, is
accompanied by an
explanatory caption.

RUNNING HEADS

These remind you which section you are in. The top of the left-hand page gives the section name, and the top of the right-hand page gives the subject heading.

ANNOTATIONS

Some pictures have annotations in *italics*. These point out the features of an illustration or diagram and usually have leader lines. Some give extra information.

CHARTS

These are used to explain structures and processes of the human body. They give a clear summary of information, such as the main parts and functions involved in a process.

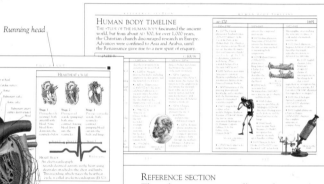

Running head

Fact box

FACT BOXES

Many pages have fact boxes. These provide interesting information about the subject, such as how long a brain cell can survive without oxygen or how many times a heart beats per year.

REFERENCE SECTION

The reference pages are yellow and appear at the back of the book. On these, you will find useful facts, figures, and charts. A timeline shows the most important events in the history of the study of the human body.

INDEX AND GLOSSARY

At the back of the book is an index listing every subject in the book. By referring to the index, information on particular topics can be found quickly. A glossary defines the technical terms used in the book.

INTRODUCTION TO THE HUMAN BODY

EVOLUTION OF THE HUMAN BODY

LIFE ON EARTH probably began four billion years ago. Single-celled organisms gradually evolved into more complex multi-celled plants and animals. Fossils suggest that human-like creatures, hominids, first appeared five million years ago.

EVOLUTIONARY CLOCK

Human life is a relatively recent occurrence in the history of life on Earth.

Earth formed 4.6 billion years ago

TIME-SCALE OF EARTH'S EXISTENCE

3.8 billion years ago

Bacteria

Marine life 1.5 billion years ago

Land plants

Dinosaurs

Humans

Apes

Orang-utan
Skull of modern monkey shows orang-utans belong to a different mammal family than either humans or apes

Sivapithecus
c.7–13 million years ago.
Extinct ancestor of the orang-utan

Chimpanzee/gorilla
Modern apes walk on all fours and have smaller brains than humans

Australopithecus
1.5–5 million years ago.
Early ape-people may have been the first to walk upright

Aegyptopithecus
30 million years ago.
Earliest known ancestor of apes and humans

HUMAN FAMILY TREE

CHANGING PROCESS

Hominids are thought to have originated in East Africa and to have been closely related to the great ape. Hominids began to lose body hair, walk upright on two feet, and use their hands to perform more complex tasks. Their brain became larger as their language and reasoning powers developed.

Homo habilis
1.5–2 million years ago.
A hunter-scavenger who had a basic form of speech

Homo erectus
0.5–1.5 million years ago.
More skilful people who lived in huts, they could produce a variety of sounds, and made fire

Performed burial ceremonies and wore animal skins

Homo sapiens neanderthalensis
30,000–200,000 years ago.
Neanderthals had overhanging brows, large noses, and undeveloped chins.

Homo sapiens sapiens
40,000 years ago.
Modern humans populated many parts of the world; they wore more refined clothes and produced art

Heavy features

Fine features

SKULLS
Fossil skulls provide the best evidence of evolution. Differences in the structure of the brow, nose, jaws, and teeth help to identify which hominid species the skull belongs to.

SKULL OF HOMO SAPIENS NEANDERTHALENSIS

SKULL OF HOMO SAPIENS SAPIENS

EVOLUTION FACTS
- About two million years ago, there were several species of hominids living at the same time.
- *Homo sapiens sapiens* is the only existing species of hominid.
- The earliest hominid fossils are from about 3.5 million years ago.

BODY SYSTEMS

THE HUMAN BODY IS made up of a number of systems.
Each one performs a particular function. All the
systems are linked together and communicate through
the blood and nervous system. Here are the major
systems of the body common to both sexes.

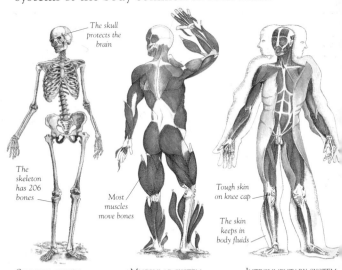

*The skull
protects the
brain*

*The
skeleton
has 206
bones*

*Most
muscles
move bones*

*Tough skin
on knee cap*

*The skin
keeps in
body fluids*

SKELETAL SYSTEM
The skeleton supports
the body and protects
the internal organs, such
as the heart and lungs.

MUSCULAR SYSTEM
All body movement
(involuntary and
voluntary) is due to the
contraction of muscles.

INTEGUMENTARY SYSTEM
Made up of skin, hair,
and nails, this system
protects the body and
keeps it waterproof.

RESPIRATORY SYSTEM
This system draws oxygenated air into the lungs and pushes out waste gases.

DIGESTIVE SYSTEM
The 9m (28 ft)-long digestive tract digests food and eliminates solid body wastes.

URINARY SYSTEM
Soluble wastes and fluids are filtered from the blood for disposal as urine.

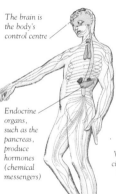

The brain is the body's control centre

Endocrine organs, such as the pancreas, produce hormones (chemical messengers)

The heart pumps blood

Vessels circulate blood

Lymph nodes filter lymph, clearing it of infection

Lymph is a pale fluid

NERVOUS SYSTEM
This sends nerve signals to and from the brain. The endocrine system carries hormonal messages.

CARDIOVASCULAR SYSTEM
Pumping blood around the body, this system provides tissues with oxygen and removes waste products.

LYMPHATIC SYSTEM
Lymph, containing immune cells, is collected by a network of lymph vessels.

CELLS

BODY SYSTEMS are made up of organs containing different tissues. A tissue is a collection of similar cells that perform a specific function. Over 200 types of specialized cell act as the body's building blocks.

CELL FEATURES

Cells contain structures called organelles ("little organs"), which carry out many vital functions. Cells are bathed in fluid, which brings them oxygen and nutrients. It also takes away products, such as hormones, and wastes, such as carbon dioxide.

CELL FACTS

• The adult human body contains over 50 trillion cells.

• Three billion of the body's cells die every minute; most are renewed.

• An egg cell (ovum) is the largest human cell. It can just be seen without a microscope.

Nucleus contains genes (units of inherited material) that instruct the cell how to grow, function, and reproduce

Nuclear membrane separates the nucleus from rest of the cell

Nuclear pores allow chemicals to move to and from the nucleus and cytoplasm

Cytoplasm is a transparent, gel-like fluid in which the organelles are suspended

Cell membrane protects the cell and separates it from its surroundings

Endoplasmic reticulum is a network of membranes that make, store, and transport substances, including proteins

Ribosomes produce proteins. They can be attached to the endoplasmic reticulum or suspended free in cytoplasm

Lysosomes are small bags of powerful chemicals that break down worn-out organelles, and digest foreign particles taken up by the cell

Mitochondria are the powerhouses of the cell where energy-releasing reactions occur

Pinocytotic vesicle – small parcel of fluid taken in by the cell and wrapped in the cell membrane

Golgi body stores and packages substances made by the cell, and transports them to the cell's surface

TYPES OF CELL

RED BLOOD CELLS
The only cells to lack a nucleus, these cells carry oxygen and live for about 120 days.

NERVE CELLS
These are the longest cells in the body. Nerve cells transport electrical messages.

WHITE BLOOD CELLS
About 10 billion new white blood cells are made every day. They help fight infection.

Nucleus

NUCLEUS STARTS TO GROW

NUCLEUS STARTS TO DIVIDE

FIRST NUCLEUS, THEN CELL, DIVIDES IN TWO

EACH CELL MAY GROW TO SIZE OF PARENT CELL

CELL DIVISION

Cells divide and multiply to allow us to grow. They divide at the fastest rate during a baby's development in the womb. In later life, when growth has stopped, cells divide at a slower rate, to replace worn-out cells.

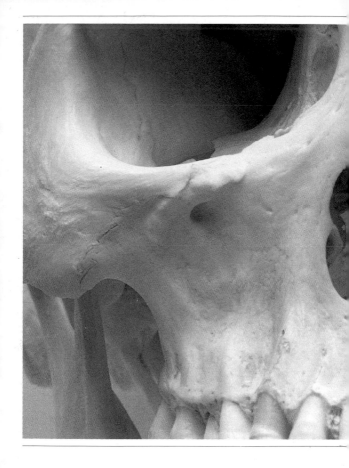

BODY STRUCTURES

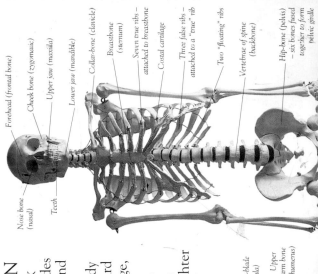

Forehead (frontal bone)

Cheek bone (zygomatic)

Upper jaw (maxilla)

Lower jaw (mandible)

Collar-bone (clavicle)

Breastbone (sternum)

Seven true ribs – attached to breastbone

Costal cartilage

Three false ribs – attached to a "true" rib

Two "floating" ribs

Vertebrae of spine (backbone)

Hip-bone (pelvis) – six bones fused together to form pelvic girdle

Nose bone (nasal)

Teeth

Skull (cranium)

Vertebrae of neck

Shoulder-blade (scapula)

Upper arm bone (humerus)

THE SKELETON

THE BODY'S FRAMEWORK is the skeleton. It provides shape and protection, and acts as an anchor for muscles to allow the body to move. Made up of hard bones and softer cartilage, the skeleton is a living tissue, and is constantly being renewed. Females usually have smaller, lighter skeletons than males.

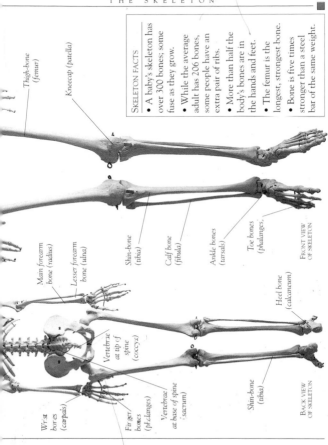

Thigh-bone
(femur)

Kneecap (patella)

SKELETON FACTS

● A baby's skeleton has over 300 bones; some fuse as they grow.

● While the average adult has 206 bones, some people have an extra pair of ribs.

● More than half the body's bones are in the hands and feet.

● The femur is the longest, strongest bone.

● Bone is five times stronger than a steel bar of the same weight.

Main forearm bone (radius)

Lesser forearm bone (ulna)

Shin-bone (tibia)

Calf bone (fibula)

Ankle bones (tarsals)

Toe bones (phalanges)

Heel bone (calcaneum)

FRONT VIEW OF SKELETON

Vertebrae at tip of spine (coccyx)

Vertebrae at base of spine (sacrum)

Wrist bones (carpals)

Finger bones (phalanges)

Shin-bone (tibia)

BACK VIEW OF SKELETON

21

BONE

MADE UP OF A NETWORK of protein fibres (collagen) filled with calcium and phosphate, bone is strong and alive. It is constantly remodelling itself, with ten per cent of its mass being replaced each year. This process involves some cells (osteoclasts) breaking down old bone, while other cells (osteoblasts) build up new bone.

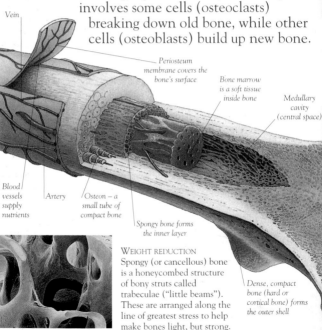

Vein

Periosteum membrane covers the bone's surface

Bone marrow is a soft tissue inside bone

Medullary cavity (central space)

Blood vessels supply nutrients

Artery

Osteon – a small tube of compact bone

Spongy bone forms the inner layer

Dense, compact bone (hard or cortical bone) forms the outer shell

WEIGHT REDUCTION
Spongy (or cancellous) bone is a honeycombed structure of bony struts called trabeculae ("little beams"). These are arranged along the line of greatest stress to help make bones light, but strong.

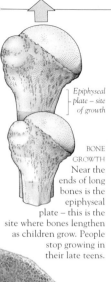

Epiphyseal plate – site of growth

BONE GROWTH

Near the ends of long bones is the epiphyseal plate – this is the site where bones lengthen as children grow. People stop growing in their late teens.

FRACTURES

A break in a bone forms a fracture. In an open (compound) fracture, the broken bone protrudes through the skin. In a closed (simple) fracture, the skin remains intact. Bone heals in several stages.

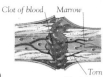

Clot of blood   Marrow

Torn blood vessels

1. A clot of blood fills the area of the fracture, 6–8 hours after the injury.

New blood vessels   Callus

2. While blood capillaries grow into the blood clot, the damaged tissue is broken down and removed. Collagen fibres start to join up the broken ends of bone. Repair tissues form a swelling called a callus.

Swelling disappears   New compact bone

Healed fracture   New spongy bone

3. Remodelling of the healing bone occurs. Repair tissue is replaced with spongy bone. Compact bone forms around the outer edge of the fracture.

BONE STRUCTURE

The skeleton has two types of bone. Compact bone, made up of tiny tubes of bone (osteons), forms the strong outer shell. Spongy bone makes up a lighter inner layer. Bone marrow is often found within spongy bone and the central space (medullary cavity) of long bones. Red marrow makes blood cells, while yellow marrow stores fat.

FACT BOX

• 99% of the body's calcium is in the bones and teeth.

• 75% of the body's bone is compact and 25% is spongy bone.

• Compact bone is the body's second hardest material after enamel.

THE SKULL

THE MOST COMPLICATED part of the skeleton is the skull. It protects the most important sense organs, and the cranial vault encases the brain. The bones of the face provide anchorage for muscles involved in facial expressions, talking, and chewing.

FRONT VIEW OF SKULL
All the bones of the skull, except the lower jaw, are locked together to make a strong box, and cannot move. The special joints between the skull bones are called sutures.

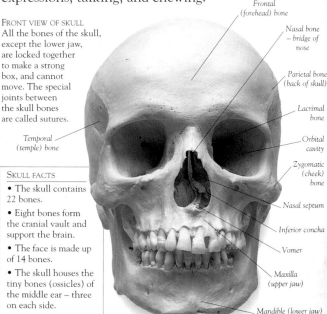

Frontal (forehead) bone

Nasal bone – bridge of nose

Parietal bone (back of skull)

Lacrimal bone

Orbital cavity

Zygomatic (cheek) bone

Nasal septum

Inferior concha

Vomer

Maxilla (upper jaw)

Mandible (lower jaw)

Temporal (temple) bone

SKULL FACTS

• The skull contains 22 bones.

• Eight bones form the cranial vault and support the brain.

• The face is made up of 14 bones.

• The skull houses the tiny bones (ossicles) of the middle ear – three on each side.

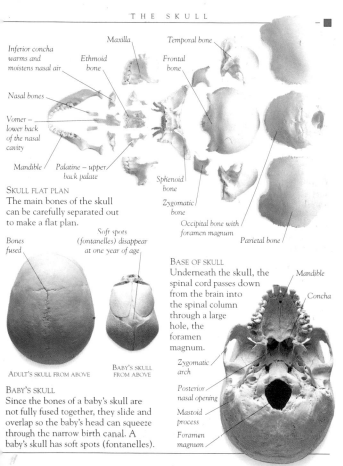

Inferior concha warms and moistens nasal air

Nasal bones

Vomer – lower back of the nasal cavity

Mandible

Ethmoid bone

Maxilla

Palatine – upper back palate

Temporal bone

Frontal bone

Sphenoid bone

Zygomatic bone

Occipital bone with foramen magnum

Parietal bone

SKULL FLAT PLAN
The main bones of the skull can be carefully separated out to make a flat plan.

Bones fused

Soft spots (fontanelles) disappear at one year of age

ADULT'S SKULL FROM ABOVE

BABY'S SKULL FROM ABOVE

BABY'S SKULL
Since the bones of a baby's skull are not fully fused together, they slide and overlap so the baby's head can squeeze through the narrow birth canal. A baby's skull has soft spots (fontanelles).

BASE OF SKULL
Underneath the skull, the spinal cord passes down from the brain into the spinal column through a large hole, the foramen magnum.

Mandible

Concha

Zygomatic arch

Posterior nasal opening

Mastoid process

Foramen magnum

THE SPINE

THE SPINAL COLUMN is one of the body's main supports. It is made up of 33 bones called vertebrae, which surround the spinal cord. The vertebrae interlock in a series of sliding joints that give the backbone flexibility. The spine has four gentle curves to give extra strength and stability.

SPINAL FACTS

• A human neck has the same number of vertebrae as a giraffe.
• Spinous processes form knobbles that protrude under the skin covering the spine.
• Intervertebral discs act as shock absorbers to prevent damage from sudden jolts.

Transverse process

Intervertebral disc

Space for nerve root

Vertebra

SKULL AND
SPINAL
COLUMN

Space for spinal cord

Small, light cervical vertebrae only need to support weight of skull

Spinous process

The first cervical vertebra, the atlas, supports the skull, allowing it free movement

The second cervical vertebra, the axis, has a peg that allows the atlas and skull to rotate and move up and down

Cancellous bone

Rib

INTERVERTEBRAL DISCS
The vertebrae are separated from each other by pads of cartilage, intervertebral discs. These have a tough, flexible outer case and a soft, jelly-like centre, and cushion and protect the vertebrae.

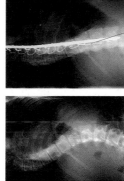

BEFORE *X-ray of excessive curvature of spine*

AFTER *Inserting a stainless steel rod helps to straighten spine*

CURVATURE OF THE SPINE
Spinal curves can become abnormally pronounced. Excessive curvature may be inwards in the lower back, outwards in the upper back, or to one side. An operation that inserts a rod may straighten the spine.

Each thoracic vertebra has two small hollows on either side to connect with a rib

Centrum (body)

Transverse process

Lumbar vertebrae are the strongest; they must support the weight of the upper body

Sacrum

Coccyx

VERTEBRA
The weight-bearing area of each vertebra is the centrum. This is attached to a ring of bone, the vertebral arch, which protects the spinal cord. Bony projections (processes) extend from the arch; the transverse processes form sliding joints.

JOINTS

TWO BONES MEET at a joint and are often held
together by bands of tissue (ligaments). Some joints
are fixed, with the bones locked together. In others,
the bones can move more freely; cartilage protects
their surfaces, which are lubricated by synovial fluid.

MOBILE JOINTS

The skeleton contains six main types of
movable joint. "Double-jointed" people
have a wider range of movement than
usual due to looser ligaments.

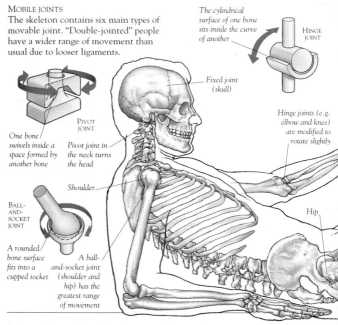

*The cylindrical
surface of one bone
sits inside the curve
of another*

HINGE
JOINT

PIVOT
JOINT

*One bone
swivels inside a
space formed by
another bone*

*Pivot joint in
the neck turns
the head*

*Fixed joint
(skull)*

*Hinge joints (e.g.
elbow and knee)
are modified to
rotate slightly*

Shoulder

Hip

BALL-
AND-
SOCKET
JOINT

*A rounded
bone surface
fits into a
cupped socket*

*A ball-
and-socket joint
(shoulder and
hip) has the
greatest range
of movement*

OTHER JOINTS

A few joints do not aid movement, but they do allow for bone growth and give protection. Other joints fit together less tightly and allow for limited flexibility.

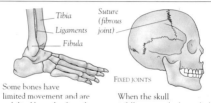

Tibia

Ligaments

Fibula

Suture (fibrous joint)

Some bones have limited movement and are stabilized by pads of cartilage, as where the tibia and fibula meet.

FIXED JOINTS

When the skull is fully grown, the bones lock together to form suture joints.

ELLIPSOIDAL JOINT

The wrist's ellipsoidal joint moves backwards and forwards or from side to side

An oval-shaped bone surface fits into an oval-shaped cup

Ellipsoidal joint

Saddle joint

SADDLE JOINT

U-shaped bone surfaces fit together at right angles to rock back and forth and side to side

The saddle joint in the thumb has limited rotation

GLIDING JOINT

Two almost flat bone surfaces move by sliding over each other

Gliding joints can be found in the hands and feet

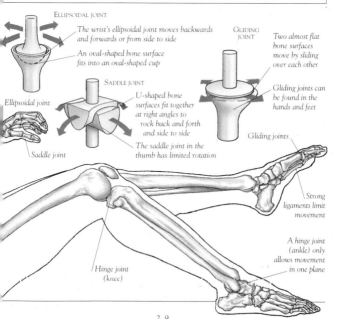

Gliding joints

Strong ligaments limit movement

A hinge joint (ankle) only allows movement in one plane

Hinge joint (knee)

Joints and movement

Joints and muscles give the body a wide range of movement. Bending a joint, such as an elbow, is known as flexion. Straightening the joint again is known as extension. Moving part of the body, such as an arm, away from the body's midline is called abduction, while drawing the arm inwards is called adduction.

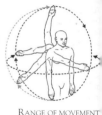

RANGE OF MOVEMENT
The shoulder ball-and-socket joint is a multiaxial joint. It moves the arm up and down, backwards and forwards, and in a circle at the side of the body.

Artery

Rectus femoris muscle

Patellar ligament

Tibia collateral ligament

Femur bone

Tibia bone

STRUCTURE OF KNEE JOINT
Internal and external ligaments stabilize the knee when it bends, and stop the ends of bones moving from side to side. Two discs of cartilage (menisci) help reduce friction between the moving bones.

Fat pad

Cruciate ligaments

Meniscus

Fibula collateral ligament

DISLOCATION
Sometimes, the ligaments supporting a mobile joint give way, as when bones are wrenched in an accident. This lets the bones slip out of place, and the joint is said to be dislocated.

Fibula bone

ARTHRITIS

Inflammation of a joint leads to pain, swelling, and deformity and is called arthritis. Rheumatoid arthritis often affects small joints; the synovial membrane becomes inflamed and later thickens.

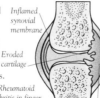

EARLY STAGE   LATE STAGE

Inflamed synovial membrane

Eroded cartilage

Rheumatoid arthritis in finger joints

Synovial membrane thickens and spreads across joint

JOINT FACTS

• The knee is the body's largest joint.

• The smallest joints link the three bones in the middle ear.

• Most large, movable joints are lubricated by synovial fluid.

• Muscles around the joints contract to produce movement.

STAGES IN OSTEOARTHRITIS

Flakes of cartilage   *Leaking of synovial fluid*

Bone marrow   *Bone*

Plug

Blood vessels

STAGE 1
When the cartilage of a joint breaks down, it is known as osteoarthritis. It usually affects the larger, weight-bearing joints such as hips and knees.

STAGE 2
Cracks in the cartilage develop and extend into the underlying bone. Blood vessels grow into the gap and secrete a clot that acts as a plug.

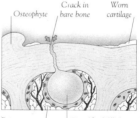

Osteophyte   *Crack in bare bone*   *Worn cartilage*

Bone marrow   *Cyst (fluid-filled cavity)*

STAGE 3
The plug wears away, allowing synovial fluid to leak in to form a cyst. The damaged bone forms swellings (osteophytes) and it becomes increasingly painful, stiff, and difficult to move the joint.

MUSCULAR SYSTEM

MUSCLES CARRY OUT all the body's voluntary and involuntary movements. Skeletal (voluntary) muscles are attached to bones either directly or through strong tendons. They tend to work in pairs; one muscle contracts while the other relaxes. This allows joints, such as the elbow, to bend or straighten.

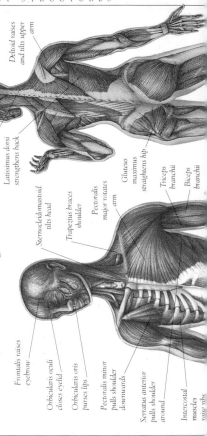

Semispinalis capitis tilts heads upwards

Deltoid raises and tilts upper arm

Trapezius pulls back head

Latissimus dorsi strengthens back

Gluteus maximus straightens hip

Triceps branchii

Biceps branchii

Sternocleidomastoid tilts head

Trapezius braces shoulder

Pectoralis major rotates arm

Frontalis raises eyebrow

Orbicularis oculi closes eyelid

Orbicularis oris purses lips

Pectoralis minor pulls shoulder downwards

Serratus anterior pulls shoulder around

Intercostal muscles raise ribs

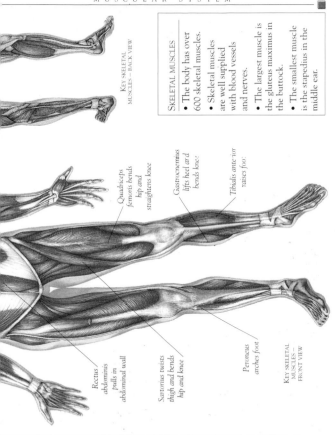

KEY SKELETAL MUSCLES – BACK VIEW

SKELETAL MUSCLES

• The body has over 600 skeletal muscles.

• Skeletal muscles are well supplied with blood vessels and nerves.

• The largest muscle is the gluteus maximus in the buttock.

• The smallest muscle is the stapedius in the middle ear.

Quadriceps femoris bends hip and straightens knee

Gastrocnemius lifts heel and bends knee

Tibialis anterior raises foot

Rectus abdominis pulls in abdominal wall

Sartorius twists thigh and bends hip and knee

Peroneus arches foot

KEY SKELETAL MUSCLES – FRONT VIEW

Muscle structures

About 40 per cent of body weight is made up of muscles. They carry out all the body's movements. Muscles have long, thin cells that convert chemical energy, found in fatty acids and blood sugar (glucose), into movement and heat. Some muscles are under voluntary control and only work consciously. Others function automatically to keep the body working smoothly.

Whole skeletal muscle

Bundle of muscle fibres (myofibres)

Single bundle of muscle fibres (myofibres)

Single myofibre

Single myofibre

Bundles of myofibrils

Myofibril

STRUCTURE

Muscles are made up of bundles of long cells (myofibres). Each myofibre contains thousands of smaller strands (myofibrils). A myofibril contains filaments of two different proteins, actin and myosin, which overlap each other. Myosin forms thicker filaments than actin.

MICROGRAPH

When looking at skeletal muscle tissue under a microscope, the interlocking filaments of actin and myosin appear as stripes.

Each repeated unit of myosin and actin is called a sarcomere

TYPES OF MUSCLE

THREE TYPES OF MUSCLE

Skeletal muscle is known as voluntary muscle; its movements are controlled consciously. Cardiac muscle is found only in the heart. Smooth muscle is known as involuntary muscle and is responsible for automatic movements within the body.

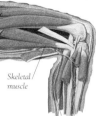

Tendon of semitendinosus muscle

Tendon of biceps femoris muscle

Skeletal muscle tapers into tendon

Achilles tendon

SKELETAL MUSCLES

While some muscles attached to the skeleton contract, others relax to produce voluntary movements, such as walking and writing.

Skeletal muscle

TENDONS

Skeletal muscle is attached to bones and other muscles through tendons. These are made of strong connective tissue.

CARDIAC MUSCLES

Muscle in the heart has branched fibres. These help electrical signals to pass through quickly, causing the heart to contract rhythmically and tirelessly.

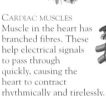

Cardiac muscle

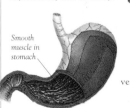

Smooth muscle in stomach

SMOOTH MUSCLES

These involuntary muscles perform automatic tasks, such as dilating or constricting blood vessels and propelling food through the stomach and gut.

MUSCLE FACTS

• Muscles can cause eyelids to blink up to five times per second.

• If too little oxygen reaches the muscles during strenuous exercise, waste lactic acid builds up, causing the muscles to ache.

Muscle action

Muscles can only pull, not push. Nerve signals from the brain instruct which muscle fibres to contract and when. For example, to pick up a weight, muscle fibres contract to produce a steady pull (isotonic contraction). To hold the weight steady once it has been picked up, muscle fibres stay the same length to produce tension (isometric contraction).

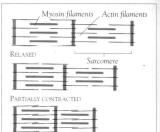

RELAXED

Sarcomere

PARTIALLY CONTRACTED

FULLY CONTRACTED

MUSCLE CONTRACTION
When a muscle fibre receives a signal, its filaments slide over each other. The fibres shorten and the muscle contracts. As the filaments slide apart again, the muscle relaxes.

MUSCLES WORKING TOGETHER
As muscles can only pull, not push, they work in pairs to move joints. To raise the lower arm, the biceps muscle contracts while the triceps muscle relaxes.

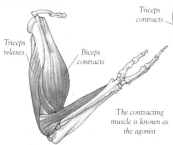

Triceps relaxes

Biceps contracts

The contracting muscle is known as the agonist

Triceps contracts

The relaxing muscle is known as the antagonist

To bring the lower arm down again, the triceps contracts and the biceps relaxes

Elbow joint straightens when biceps relaxes

BUILDING UP MUSCLE

Bodybuilders exercise their muscles repeatedly to build up their bulk. Each muscle becomes highly toned with strong tendons and an increased blood supply. Eating starchy foods and proteins helps increase bulk.

Highly developed muscles

FEMALE BODYBUILDER

TORN MUSCLE

Excessive strain on a muscle can damage muscle fibres. This causes pain, swelling, and loss of movement. When a muscle tears, the rich network of blood vessels in the muscle bleeds. If the blood builds up, it may need to be drained.

Deltoid muscle

Muscle tear due to excessive movements of shoulder joint

Humerus bone

FACIAL MUSCLES

FACIAL MUSCLES

The face has over 30 muscles, which relax and contract to express a variety of emotions from pleasure and surprise to anger and confusion.

FROWNING

Muscles (corrugator supercilii) above each eye pull the forehead down into a frown.

SURPRISE

A large muscle in the forehead (frontalis) contracts to raise the eyebrows in surprise.

GLUMNESS

A large, flat sheet of muscle (platysma) fans out down the neck and pulls the mouth down.

MUSCLE PROBLEMS

PROBLEM	DESCRIPTION
Myalgia	Muscle pain due to infection or inflammation.
Tendinitis	Inflammation of a tendon due to over use or injury.
Cramp	Prolonged spasm due to the build-up of waste lactic acid.
Tetanus	Prolonged spasm due to a bacterial infection.
Muscular dystrophy	An inherited wasting disease.

HAIR AND NAILS

THE SKIN PRODUCES specialized structures made of the tough protein, keratin. Nails strengthen and shield the tips of fingers and toes. Hair provides warmth, and protects most areas of the skin.

STRUCTURE
The outer surface of each hair is coated with dead cells that protect the hair.

HAIR TYPES
Whether hair grows straight, wavy, or curly depends on the shape of the hair follicle.

Curly hair grows from an oval follicle

Wavy hair grows from a flat follicle

Straight hair grows from a round follicle

Hair sheath projects above skin's outer layer (epidermis)

Dermis

Erector muscle

Follicle (hair pit)

HAIR FOLLICLES
Hairs are tubes of keratin that grow from follicles in the lower layer (dermis) of the skin. There are about 100,000 hair follicles on the head.

BALDNESS
Male-pattern baldness can be inherited, but most men start to lose their hair as they get older. Hair often starts to recede from the front or the crown.

Receding hairline forms "widow's peak" at the front

Hair also starts to recede from the crown

Hair loss meets to produce baldness over the top of the head

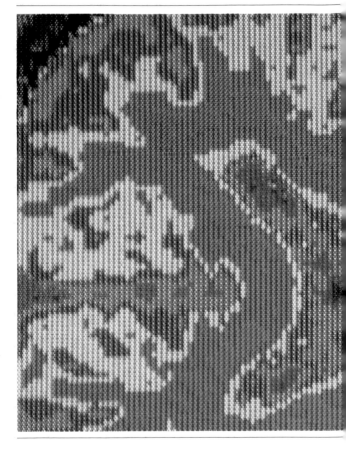

NAIL STRUCTURE

Keratin, the hard, fibrous protein that makes up nails, is produced by active cells at the base and sides of each nail. These growing areas are protected by folds of skin, called cuticles.

Cuticle covers the nail's growing areas

Nail moon (lunula) contains some nail-making cells

Nail bed looks pink because of underlying blood vessels

HAIR AND NAIL FACTS

• About 80 scalp hairs fall out per day.

• Fingernails take over six months to grow from base to tip.

• When it is cold, erector muscles pull each hair upright; this traps air and produces "goose-bumps".

NAIL GROWTH

Nails grow up to 5 mm (0.2 in) per month. Some people have strong nails; if not cut, they can grow up to 30 cm (12 in) long.

SOME NAIL AND HAIR PROBLEMS	
NAME	DESCRIPTION
Whitlows	Small abscesses at the side of the nail.
Black nails	Hard knocks cause bruising and black nails.
Fungal infection	Fungus grows through the nail plate, making it brittle and distorted.
Brittle nails	Nails split and break easily, sometimes due to lack of iron.
Alopecia universalis	Loss of hair extends all over the body, including eyebrows and eyelashes.
Alopecia areata	Loss of hair produces one or more patches of baldness on the scalp. May be caused by emotional stress.

BRAIN AND NERVOUS SYSTEM

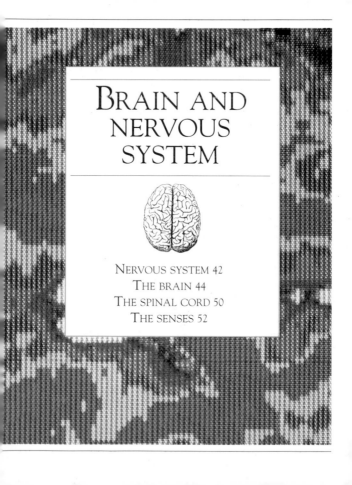

NERVOUS SYSTEM

THE BRAIN and the spinal cord make up the central nervous system (CNS). This interlinks with the peripheral nervous system, which forms a network of nerve fibres throughout the rest of the body. These two systems work together to co-ordinate the body's actions.

NERVE FACTS

- All the body's nerves laid end to end would measure about 75 km (47 miles).
- The sciatic nerve is the longest nerve.
- Nerve signals can travel at over 400 km/h (248 mph).
- Pain signals travel more slowly than touch signals.

NERVE NETWORK

Nerve fibres run together in cables to form nerve trunks. These divide and branch into smaller nerves reaching every part of the body. Some nerves group together and interweave to form a plexus.

Optic nerve

Brachial plexus

Radial nerve

Vagus nerve

Phrenic nerve

Lateral pectoral nerve

Intercostal nerves

Subcostal nerve

Iliohypogastric nerve

Spinal cord

Supraclavicular nerve

Axillary nerve

Radial nerve

Spinal ganglion

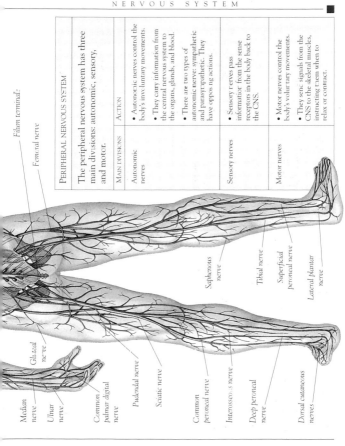

PERIPHERAL NERVOUS SYSTEM

The peripheral nervous system has three main divisions: autonomic, sensory, and motor.

MAIN DIVISIONS	ACTION
Autonomic nerves	• Autonomic nerves control the body's involuntary movements. • They carry information from the central nervous system to the organs, glands, and blood. • There are two types of autonomic nerve: sympathetic and parasympathetic. They have opposing actions.
Sensory nerves	• Sensory nerves pass information from the sense receptors in the body back to the CNS.
Motor nerves	• Motor nerves control the body's voluntary movements. • They send signals from the CNS to the skeletal muscles, instructing them when to relax or contract.

Filum terminale

Femoral nerve

Median nerve

Ulnar nerve

Gluteal nerve

Common palmar digital nerve

Pudendal nerve

Sciatic nerve

Common peroneal nerve

Saphenous nerve

Interosseous nerve

Deep peroneal nerve

Dorsal cutaneous nerves

Tibial nerve

Superficial peroneal nerve

Lateral plantar nerve

THE BRAIN

THE BODY'S MAIN control centre is the brain. It is encased in the bony skull and floats in a pool of cerebrospinal fluid, which gives extra protection by absorbing shock waves. The brain communicates with the rest of the body through the cranial nerves and the spinal cord.

LEFT   RIGHT

HEMISPHERES
The brain is made up of two halves: the right and left hemispheres. The left side is usually dominant and controls logic and speech, while the right side produces creative thoughts.

Right cerebral hemisphere

White matter – made up of nerve fibres

Protective skull

Nasal cavity

Grey matter (cortex) – made up of nerve cell bodies

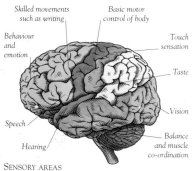

Skilled movements such as writing

Basic motor control of body

Behaviour and emotion

Touch sensation

Taste

Vision

Speech

Balance and muscle co-ordination

Hearing

SENSORY AREAS
The brain is divided into several regions – each has its own important function. Some regions, known as sensory areas, receive information from sense organs and receptors. They are involved in interpreting sensations. Other parts, known as motor areas, control the movement of voluntary muscles.

STRUCTURE

There are three major parts of the brain. The largest, the cerebrum, is divided into two hemispheres. The cerebellum, at the rear of the brain, is also made up of two tightly folded halves. The brain stem connects the brain to the spinal cord.

HUMAN BRAIN

APE BRAIN

BIRD BRAIN

BRAIN POWER AND SIZE

Humans have the most complex brain of all animals. It gives humans the power of original thought and communication through speech and writing. It is heavier in relation to body weight than the brain of any other animal.

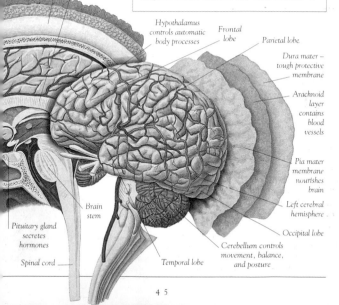

Periosteum (skull membrane)

Corpus callosum – bundle of nerve fibres that link two hemispheres

Hypothalamus controls automatic body processes

Frontal lobe

Parietal lobe

Dura mater – tough protective membrane

Arachnoid layer contains blood vessels

Pia mater membrane nourishes brain

Left cerebral hemisphere

Occipital lobe

Brain stem

Pituitary gland secretes hormones

Spinal cord

Temporal lobe

Cerebellum controls movement, balance, and posture

Neurons

The nervous system has specialized cells called neurons, which carry electrical (nerve) impulses. Motor neurons transport signals from the brain and spinal cord, and sensory neurons carry signals from the body to the central nervous system.

Dendrite receives impulses coming into the cell

Synaptic knob at end of axon

Axon carries impulses away from cell

Nucleus *Cell body*

Glial cells form fatty sheath

STRUCTURE
Neuron cell bodies have dendrites projections that receive impulses coming into the cell. They also have axons, fine filaments that carry electrical impulses away from the cell body.

TYPES OF NEURON
Unipolar neurons have a single axon which branches; bipolar neurons has one axon and one dendrite; and multipolar neurons have an axon and a varying number of dendrites.

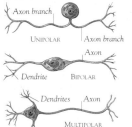

Axon branch

UNIPOLAR | *Axon branch*

Axon

Dendrite BIPOLAR

Dendrites *Axon*

MULTIPOLAR

GLIAL CELLS
Neurons are supported by glial cells, which do not carry electrical impulses. Some destroy infection, some insulate axons, while others control the flow of fluid and nutrients to the nerve cells.

Oligodendrocytes wrap around some axons to form fatty, insulating sheaths

Astrocytes transfer nourishment from the blood to the brain and spinal cord

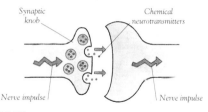

Synaptic knob

Chemical neurotransmitters

Nerve impulse

Nerve impulse

SYNAPSE

An axon of one cell meets a dendrite of another at a tiny gap called a synapse. Here nerve impulses are converted into chemical neurotransmitters. Once across the synapse, they change back into electrical impulses.

BRAIN BEHAVIOUR

• One brain cell can connect to 25,000 other brain cells.

• Neurons cannot divide and multiply like other cells.

• When neurons die, they are not replaced.

• If a brain cell is deprived of oxygen, it dies after 5 minutes.

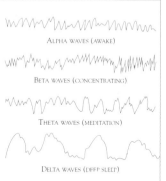

ALPHA WAVES (AWAKE)

BETA WAVES (CONCENTRATING)

THETA WAVES (MEDITATION)

DELTA WAVES (DEEP SLEEP)

BRAINWAVE RECORDINGS

Every second, millions of nerve impulses pass from neuron to neuron in the brain. This produces an electrical field; the brain's level of activity can be recorded as an electroencephalogram (EEG).

A baby needs 14–16 hours sleep a day

A three-year-old needs 12 hours sleep

An adult gets on average about 7.5 hours sleep each night

SLEEP

Neuron activity increases while the body sleeps. There are two types of sleep: rapid-eye-movement (REM) sleep, in which the eyes move constantly, and slow-wave sleep. There are four stages in slow-wave sleep – stage 1 is the lightest and stage 4 the deepest. Most dreaming occurs during REM sleep.

Cranial nerves

Twelve pairs of major nerves originate in the brain and its stem. These cranial nerves carry motor signals to muscles in the head and neck region, or carry sensory information back to the brain from the sense organs. Others control facial expressions.

BASE OF THE BRAIN

Olfactory nerve (I) carries smell signals

Trigeminal nerve (V) has three sensory branches

Facial nerve (VII) carries motor and sensory fibres

Spinal accessory nerve (XI) helps with speech

Optic nerve (II) helps vision

Oculomotor (III), abducent (VI), and trochlear (IV) nerves control eye movement

Vestibulo-cochlear nerve (VIII) helps hearing and balance

Hypoglossal (XII) nerves and glossopharyngeal (IX) nerves

Vagus nerve (X) – the wanderer

CRANIAL NERVES

• Vagus means "the wanderer" as this nerve travels through the torso (upper body).

• Cranial nerves form part of the peripheral nervous system.

• Nine of the twelve nerves carry messages to the muscles.

STRUCTURE
Numbered using Roman numerals I to XII, the cranial nerves are paired and form symmetrical structures on the underside of the brain. The cranial nerves that leave the head pass through holes in the base of the skull.

CRANIAL NERVES

BASE OF
THE BRAIN

FUNCTIONS
Each nerve has a number
of important functions.
Some are involved in
sight, hearing, balance,
smell, or taste sensations.

*Nerve carries information
from taste buds to the brain*

*Controls salivation,
tear production, and
facial muslces*

FACIAL NERVE (VII)

Olfactory centre

*Nerve carries
information from
smell receptors in the
nose to the olfactory
centre of the brain*

OLFACTORY NERVE (I)

*Inner ear contains
sense organs*

*Nerves carry information
about hearing and balance
from the inner ear*

VESTIBULOCOCHLEAR
NERVE (VIII)

OPTIC
NERVE
(II)

*Nerve carries
information from
light receptors in
the retina of the eye
to visual centres in
the brain*

*Nerves control muscles
used in swallowing*

*Involved in taste, touch,
and temperature sensation
in the mouth*

GLOSSOPHARYNGEAL (IX)
AND HYPOGLOSSAL NERVES (XII)

OCULOMOTOR (III),
TROCHLEAR (IV), AND
ABDUCENT NERVES
(VI)

*Focus
pupil and lens*

*Three pairs
of eye nerves
control
voluntary
movements
of the eye
muscles*

*Nerve regulates many
automatic functions such as
the heart rate, breathing, and
the making of stomach acid*

Also involved in speech

VAGUS NERVE (X)

*Each nerve has three
branches, which supply
sensation to parts of
the face and control
chewing muscles*

TRIGEMINAL NERVE (V)

*Nerve controls voluntary
muscles that move the
head and the neck*

*This nerve is also
involved in speech*

SPINAL ACCESSORY NERVE (XI)

THE SPINAL CORD

A THICK BUNDLE of nerve fibres emerges through a hole (foramen magnum) in the base of the skull to form the spinal cord. Protected by cerebrospinal fluid, three membranes, and the bony vertebrae, the spinal cord extends from the brain. It relays information between the brain and various parts of the body.

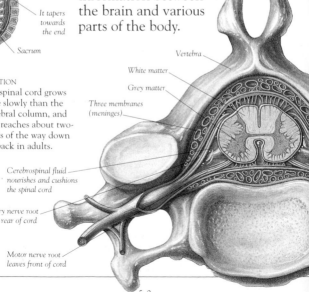

The spinal cord is protected by vertebrae

It occupies the first two-thirds of the vertebral column

It tapers towards the end

Sacrum

POSITION
The spinal cord grows more slowly than the vertebral column, and only reaches about two-thirds of the way down the back in adults.

Vertebra

White matter

Grey matter

Three membranes (meninges)

Cerebrospinal fluid nourishes and cushions the spinal cord

Sensory nerve root leaves rear of cord

Motor nerve root leaves front of cord

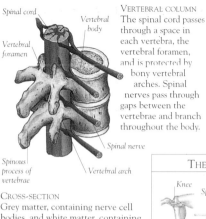

VERTEBRAL COLUMN

The spinal cord passes through a space in each vertebra, the vertebral foramen, and is protected by bony vertebral arches. Spinal nerves pass through gaps between the vertebrae and branch throughout the body.

Spinal cord

Vertebral body

Vertebral foramen

Spinal nerve

Spinous process of vertebrae

Vertebral arch

SPINAL CORD FACTS

• An adult's spinal cord is about 43 cm (17 in) long.

• The spinal cord is 2 cm (0.8 in) thick.

• The spinal cord stops growing at about the age of 4 or 5.

• Fat gives white matter its colour.

CROSS-SECTION

Grey matter, containing nerve cell bodies, and white matter, containing nerve cell filaments (axons) surrounded by fatty sheaths, make up the spinal cord. Sensory fibres from the rear of the cord join motor fibres from the front to form 31 pairs of spinal nerves.

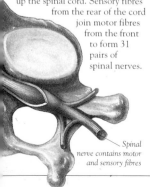

Spinal nerve contains motor and sensory fibres

THE KNEE-JERK REFLEX

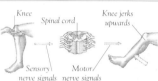

Knee

Spinal cord

Knee jerks upwards

Sensory nerve signals

Motor nerve signals

Stage 1
Tapping the tendon below the kneecap stretches the knee down.

Stage 2
Sensory stretch signals pass to spinal cord, and trigger reflex motor signals.

Stage 3
Muscles in the lower thigh contract, jerking the knee upwards.

REFLEX ARC

A spinal reflex is an involuntary response to a stimulus involving a nerve loop (reflex arc) that passes through the spinal cord. This produces a fast response to overcome possible dangers. Signals reach the brain several milliseconds later. A good example of a spinal reflex arc is the knee-jerk reflex of the lower leg.

THE SENSES

SENSORY RECEPTORS help to detect stimuli from inside and outside the body. As well as the five special senses of taste, smell, hearing, balance, and sight, there are other general senses, such as touch and pain.

The skin

Forming a waterproof barrier, the skin protects the body from physical damage and infection. It is also sensitive to touch, helps to control body temperature, and repairs itself.

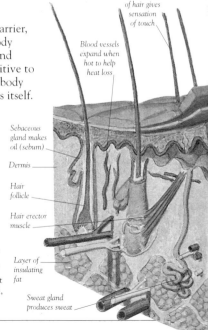

Movement of hair gives sensation of touch

Blood vessels expand when hot to help heat loss

Sebaceous gland makes oil (sebum)

Dermis

Hair follicle

Hair erector muscle

Layer of insulating fat

Sweat gland produces sweat

MERKEL'S DISC

FREE NERVE ENDING

RUFFINI'S CORPUSCLE

SENSORY NERVE ENDINGS
The skin contains a variety of nerve endings that detect light touch, sustained pressure, cold, warmth, or pain. They send electrical signals to the brain.

Fingerprints

Months before birth, ridges of skin form on the fingertips. Arranged in unique patterns of whorls and loops, these ridges help to grip slippery surfaces and contain sweat ducts. No two people have the same fingerprints.

WHORL

ARCH

COMPOSITE

LOOP

Epidermis contains layers of flattened skin cells

Basal layer of epidermis produces new cells

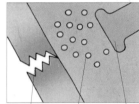

Damaged tissue | *Chemicals* | *Nerve ending*

Pain Receptors

When tissue is damaged, cells release chemicals. These activate the bare nerve endings that detect pain.

Sense receptor

Structure

The skin has two main layers: an outer epidermis and an inner dermis. New cells move from the base of the epidermis to the surface, where they harden and die to produce a tough, waterproof layer. The dermis is living and contains nerves, blood vessels, sense receptors, glands, and hair follicles.

The tongue

Used in talking, eating, and tasting, the
tongue is a muscular structure. It contains
taste buds that detect chemicals in food
and drink. The tongue's sense of taste
works with the nose's
sense of smell to
identify food
flavours.

TONGUE SURFACE MAGNIFIED

STRUCTURE
Taste buds
(receptor
cells) are
located on
small bumps on
the surface of the
tongue, called
papillae. They
detect the four basic
flavours – sweet, sour,
bitter, and salty.

Bitterness is
tasted at the back
of the tongue

No taste buds in
the centre

Sourness is
tasted along the
edges at the back

Saltiness is tasted along
the sides at the front

Sweetness is tasted
at the front

TASTE FACTS

• A baby has taste
buds all over the
inside of the mouth.

• There are over
10,000 taste buds on
the tongue.

• Taste bud cells
only last a week before
being renewed.

Taste pore

Taste hairs

TASTE BUD
Sensory hairs project from
cells into the central pore of
the taste bud. Here, they dip
into chemicals dissolved in
saliva and detect any taste.

Nerve
fibres

Tongue
tissue

The nose

The sense of smell detects substances that release airborne molecules. These dissolve in nasal mucus and stimulate hair-like endings (cilia) inside the nose. Processed by the same part of the brain that deals with memory and emotions, smells can produce strong emotional responses.

STRUCTURE

The nose is separated into two halves by a wall, the septum. The nasal cavity is lined with hairs and membranes that secrete sticky mucus. The cilia on the receptor cells (olfactory cells) are located high in the nasal cavity.

Cilia cover the olfactory bulb and are sensitive to chemicals in mucus

Olfactory nerve sends messages to the brain

The nose warms and moistens air before it reaches the lungs

Nasal hairs filter particles as they are breathed in

Mucus, secreted by a mucous membrane, picks up chemicals in the air

SMELL

The sense of smell is strongest at birth and helps a baby to recognize its mother. This graph shows how the sense of smell declines with increasing age.

SENSE OF SMELL CHART

82%	38%	28%
AGE 20	AGE 60	AGE 80

SMELL FACTS

• The sense of smell can detect 2,000–4,000 different odours.

• Sniffing draws molecules up to the smell receptors for analysis.

• The brain grows used to smells quickly and stops registering them.

The ear

The senses of hearing and balance involve the stimulation of hair receptor cells in the inner ear. Sounds are created by waves of pressure that cause air to vibrate. These vibrations trigger a chain of movement from the outer ear to the inner ear, where hair cells send electrical impulses to the brain for analysis.

EAR STRUCTURE
The ear is divided into three parts: the outer, middle, and inner ears. The outer ear consists of the pinna and auditory canal. The delicate parts of the ear are protected by the bones of the skull.

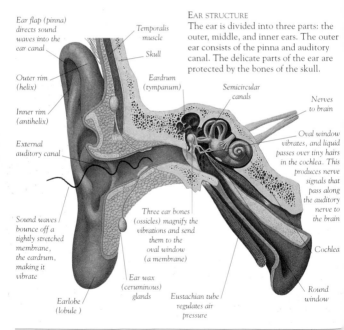

Ear flap (pinna) directs sound waves into the ear canal

Temporalis muscle

Skull

Eardrum (tympanum)

Semicircular canals

Nerves to brain

Outer rim (helix)

Inner rim (antihelix)

External auditory canal

Oval window vibrates, and liquid passes over tiny hairs in the cochlea. This produces nerve signals that pass along the auditory nerve to the brain

Sound waves bounce off a tightly stretched membrane, the eardrum, making it vibrate

Three ear bones (ossicles) magnify the vibrations and send them to the oval window (a membrane)

Cochlea

Ear wax (ceruminous) glands

Eustachian tube regulates air pressure

Round window

Earlobe (lobule)

MIDDLE EAR

Within this air-filled space are three tiny bones: the hammer (malleus), anvil (incus), and stirrup (stapes). Air pressure across the eardrum is regulated by the Eustachian tube, which links the middle ear to the throat.

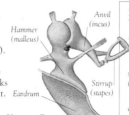

Hammer (malleus)

Anvil (incus)

Stirrup (stapes)

Eardrum

EAR FACTS

- Humans can distinguish over 1,500 musical tones.
- People can hear sounds ranging from 0–140 decibels.
- Ears can detect the direction of sound within 3 degrees.
- The smallest bone in the body is the stirrup.

Fluid (perilymph) in labyrinth of channels

Nerves

Cochlea

Semicircular canals

INNER EAR

The labyrinth, or inner ear, contains the sound-detecting cochlea and three semicircular canals. Hair cells sense motion and vibration, and send nerve impulses to the brain.

NOISE LEVELS

Loudness of sound is measured in decibels (dB). Sounds above 130dB can cause vibration damage to the ear and may lead to deafness.

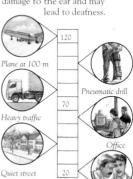

Plane at 100 m

Heavy traffic

Quiet street

Pneumatic drill

Office

Whispering

120

70

20

Decibels

NOISE LEVEL COMPARISONS

BALANCE

Hair receptors respond to the flow of fluid within the semicircular canals. They detect changes in movement.

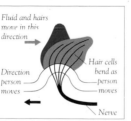

Fluid and hairs move in this direction

Direction person moves

Hair cells bend as person moves

Nerve

The eye

Sight is one of the most important senses. When light enters the eye, the lens focuses it upside-down onto the retina. The image stimulates light-sensitive cells called rods and cones, which send signals to the brain. Rods detect dim light but only register black and white. Cones give colour vision.

CROSS-SECTION OF EYE

Conjunctiva (thin membrane of skin) keeps eye moist

Pigments in iris give colour

Pupil – light enters hole

Cornea

Aqueous humour – watery fluid

Lens

Muscular ring controls shape of lens

Vitreous humour – jelly-like fluid

Retina contains photoreceptors that detect light

Choroid supplies eye with blood

Optic nerve leads to brain

Sclera

EYE FACTS

• Colour blindness affects around 1 person in 30, but affects as many as 1 in 12 men.

• The human eye can detect a lighted candle 1.6 km (1 mile) away.

• Humans blink about 15 times per minute.

• A person can see up to 10,000 colours.

EYE STRUCTURE

The spherical eyeball is divided by the lens into two fluid-filled compartments. Its surface has three layers: the tough outer sclera (white of eye); the choroid, composed of blood vessels; and the retina, containing light-sensitive cells. The transparent cornea protects the front of the eye and helps to focus light.

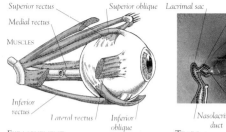

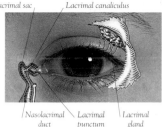

EYE MOVEMENT

Six muscles attached to the sclera move the eyeball. Movements are co-ordinated so both eyes look in the same direction. If a muscle is weak, the eyes may move separately, causing a squint.

TEARS

The washing action of tears keeps the eyes moist and free from infection. Tears contain lysozyme, a chemical that helps to kill bacteria. Excess tears drain down the nasolacrimal duct into the nose.

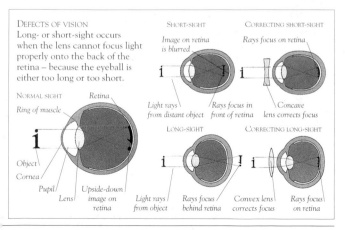

DEFECTS OF VISION

Long- or short-sight occurs when the lens cannot focus light properly onto the back of the retina – because the eyeball is either too long or too short.

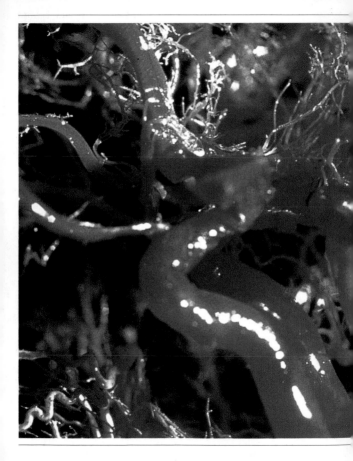

HEART, BLOOD, AND LUNGS

CARDIOVASCULAR SYSTEM

MADE UP OF THE HEART, blood, and blood vessels, the cardiovascular system supplies every part of the body with oxygen, nutrients, and chemicals that regulate the body's processes. It also carries away wastes and carbon dioxide. Arteries transport blood away from the heart, while veins carry blood to the heart.

BLOOD AND VESSELS
• The circulatory system contains around 150,000 km (93,000 miles) of blood vessels.
• The heart pumps about 13,640 litres (3,000 gallons) of blood per day.
• The aorta is the largest artery; the vena cava is the largest vein.

Temporal artery

Facial artery

Common carotid artery

External jugular vein

Thyroid vein

Axillary vein

Superior vena cava

Pulmonary arteries

Aorta

Heart

Descending aorta

Inferior vena cava

Superior mesenteric artery

Pulmonary veins

Radial artery

Ulnar artery

Common hepatic artery

Gastric artery

Common iliac artery

Common iliac vein

Pulmonary venous arch

Digital vein

Great saphenous vein

Femoral vein

Popliteal vein

Perforating veins

Posterior tibial vein

Small saphenous vein

Plantar venous arch

Dorsal venous arch

Dorsal digital vein

Arterial network of knee

Posterior tibial artery

Anterior tibial artery

Plantar arteries

Dorsal metatarsal artery

Deep femoral artery

Femoral circumflex artery

Femoral artery

DOUBLE CIRCULATION

Superior vena cava

Arm

Head

Aorta

Arm

Lung

Heart

Lung

Liver

Kidney

Inferior vena cava

Digestive tract

Kidney

Legs

The pulmonary circulation pumps deoxygenated blood from the heart to the lungs and back to the heart. The systemic circulation pumps oxygenated blood from the heart to the rest of the body.

THE HEART

ACTING AS A DOUBLE PUMP, the heart is a fist-sized muscular organ divided into a left and a right side. Each side contains two chambers: an upper atrium and a lower ventricle. These chambers contract and relax about 70 times a minute to keep blood flowing around the body.

THE HEART LIES IN THE MIDDLE OF THE CHEST

STRUCTURE

A thick, muscular wall called the septum separates the two sides of the heart. Although the atria have thinner walls than the ventricles, all the chambers hold the same volume of blood, 70–80 ml (2.5–2.8 fl oz).

OPEN VALVE   CLOSED VALVE

HEART VALVES

The four main heart valves (mitral, tricuspid, pulmonary, and aortic) open to let blood through, then close to prevent back-flow. This keeps blood moving in the same direction.

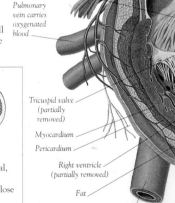

Superior vena cava

Right atrium

Pulmonary vein carries oxygenated blood

Tricuspid valve (partially removed)

Myocardium

Pericardium

Right ventricle (partially removed)

Fat

Inferior vena cava

Aorta

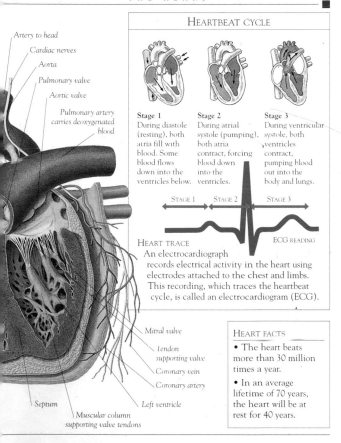

Artery to head

Cardiac nerves

Aorta

Pulmonary valve

Aortic valve

Pulmonary artery
carries deoxygenated
blood

HEARTBEAT CYCLE

Stage 1
During diastole
(resting), both
atria fill with
blood. Some
blood flows
down into the
ventricles below.

Stage 2
During atrial
systole (pumping),
both atria
contract, forcing
blood down
into the
ventricles.

Stage 3
During ventricular
systole, both
ventricles
contract,
pumping blood
out into the
body and lungs.

← STAGE 1 → ← STAGE 2 → ← STAGE 3 →

ECG READING

HEART TRACE
An electrocardiograph
records electrical activity in the heart using
electrodes attached to the chest and limbs.
This recording, which traces the heartbeat
cycle, is called an electrocardiogram (ECG).

Mitral valve

Tendon
supporting valve

Coronary vein

Coronary artery

Left ventricle

Septum

Muscular column
supporting valve tendons

HEART FACTS

• The heart beats
more than 30 million
times a year.

• In an average
lifetime of 70 years,
the heart will be at
rest for 40 years.

BLOOD

ALL TISSUES IN THE BODY receive a blood supply, even the bones. Blood is made up of plasma, a watery fluid in which float billions of red blood cells (erythrocytes), white blood cells (leucocytes), and cell fragments (platelets). Plasma also contains dissolved salts, hormones, fats, sugars, and proteins.

Platelet

BLOOD CELLS
In order to supply the body with oxygen, red blood cells are shaped to squeeze through the narrowest blood vessel, a capillary.

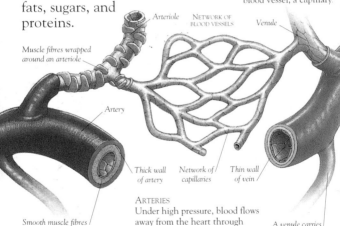

NETWORK OF BLOOD VESSELS

Arteriole

Venule

Muscle fibres wrapped around an arteriole

Artery

Thick wall of artery

Network of capillaries

Thin wall of vein

Smooth muscle fibres help the artery dilate and contract to regulate blood flow

ARTERIES
Under high pressure, blood flows away from the heart through arteries, which have thick, elastic walls. Most arteries, except those taking blood to the lungs, carry bright red, oxygenated blood.

A venule carries deoxygenated blood

VEINS

Carrying blood back to the heart under relatively low pressure, veins have thinner walls than arteries. Most veins, except those taking blood from the lungs, carry deoxygenated blood, which looks blue.

A venule is a small vein

Valve in the vein stops blood from flowing backwards

A venule branches off a vein

BLOOD VESSELS

Arteries branch into smaller arterioles connected to a web of capillaries. These have thin walls through which oxygen and nutrients can pass. The capillaries return deoxygenated blood to venules, which feed into larger vein trunks.

DIRECTION OF BLOOD FLOW THROUGH VESSELS

Vein

Artery

Muscle fibres

Arteriole

Capillary

Venule

BLOOD CLOTTING

When tissue is damaged, a clot forms to stop the bleeding.

Fibrin threads

Skin

Platelet

Red blood cell

Blood vessel

Damaged tissues release chemicals that attract platelets. These stick together and trigger the formation of a fibrin web.

White blood cells attack invading germs

Scab

Platelet

Red blood cells become trapped in the web, forming a clot. This dries, leaving a scab to protect the healing wound.

FIGHTING INFECTION

THE BODY'S DEFENCES against infection include the skin barrier and the production of germ-fighting chemicals and cells. These immune cells patrol the whole body, but are concentrated in the lymphatic tissues. Fluid from blood drains into the body tissues and then into the lymphatic system, where it is filtered and returned to the bloodstream.

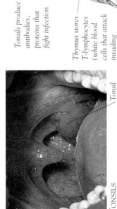

VESSELS AND ORGANS OF THE LYMPHATIC SYSTEM

Supratrochlear node drains lower arm

Axillary node drains upper arm

Thoracic duct drains into left subclavian vein and returns lymph to bloodstream

Spleen stores lymphocytes

Cysterna chyli – slender sac leading into thoracic duct

Adenoid glands produce antibodies

Tonsils produce antibodies, proteins that fight infection

Thymus stores T-lymphocytes (white blood cells that attack invading organisms)

Tonsil

TONSILS
When infection is present in the mouth's lymphatic fluid, the tonsils swell and become painful as immune cells multiply to fight the invaders.

68

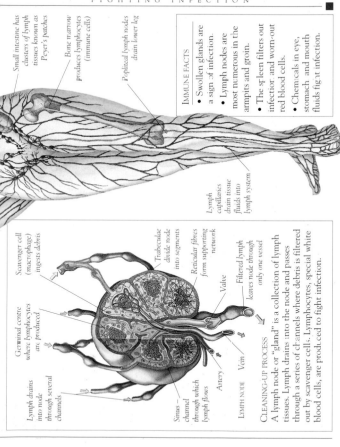

Small intestine has clusters of lymph tissues known as Peyer's patches

Bone marrow produces lymphocytes (immune cells)

Popliteal lymph nodes drain lower leg

Lymph capillaries drain tissue fluids into lymph system

IMMUNE FACTS
• Swollen glands are a sign of infection.
• Lymph nodes are most numerous in the armpits and groin.
• The spleen filters out infection and worn-out red blood cells.
• Chemicals in eye, stomach and mouth fluids fight infection.

Lymph drains into node through several channels

Germinal centre where lymphocytes are produced

Scavenger cell (macrophage) ingests debris

Trabeculae divide node into segments

Reticular fibres form supporting network

Valve

Filtered lymph leaves node through only one vessel

Sinus – channel through which lymph flows

Artery

Vein

LYMPH NODE

CLEANING-UP PROCESS
A lymph node or "gland" is a collection of lymph tissues. Lymph drains into the node and passes through a series of channels where debris is filtered out by scavenger cells. Lymphocytes, special white blood cells, are produced to fight infection.

The immune system

Specialized immune cells are designed to protect against disease by attacking "foreign" invaders, including bacteria, viruses, and foreign proteins such as poisons and transplanted tissues. Body cells have distinctive membranes. This helps immune cells recognize and ignore normal cells, but destroy infected or cancerous ones.

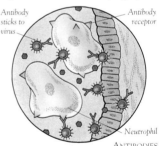

Neutrophil engulfs virus

Neutrophil

Ingested virus destroyed by chemicals

PHAGOCYTOSIS
Some immune cells, such as neutrophils and macrophages, can engulf invading organisms. This is known as phagocytosis.

Antibody sticks to virus

Antibody receptor

Neutrophil

ANTIBODIES
B-cells make antibodies, which recognize and stick to invading organisms, such as a virus. These antibodies can stick to special receptors on neutrophils to speed up the process of phagocytosis.

WHITE BLOOD CELLS	

All immune cells are made in the bone marrow or thymus gland. They secrete chemical alarm signals called cytokines. These quickly attract other patrolling immune cells into an area for a swift immune response.

NAME	FUNCTION
Neutrophils	Making up about 60% of circulating white blood cells, these engulf bacteria.
Macrophages	Scavenger cells hunt down and engulf unwanted tissue debris and foreign matter.
B-lymphocytes (B-cells)	Each B-lymphocyte makes a single, specific type of antibody.
T-lymphocytes (T-cells)	These control antibody production by B-cells and also attack infected cells.

IMMUNIZATION

Active immunization protects the body for years by injecting harmless extracts that mimic infection. Passive immunization injects antibodies taken from recently infected people and lasts only a few weeks.

ACTIVE IMMUNIZATION

Vaccine injected under the skin

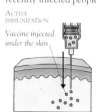

A vaccine contains harmless or dead organisms that cannot cause disease.

Antibody   *Vaccine*

A vaccine stimulates the production of antibodies by B-cells.

Real infection

The vaccine allows for a more rapid immune response if the real disease is encountered.

PASSIVE IMMUNIZATION

Antibodies are extracted

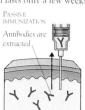

Volunteers donate blood containing antibodies.

Antibodies

The donated antibodies are injected into the patient.

Real infection

If disease organisms attack in the near future, the donated antibodies mop them up.

IMMUNE FACTS

- Neutrophils only live 6–20 hours.

- Macrophage literally means "big eater".

- B-lymphocytes are made in bone marrow.

- T-lymphocytes are derived from the thymus gland.

AIDS VIRUS

HIV (human immuno-deficiency virus) causes AIDS (acquired immune deficiency syndrome). T-helper cells, which help other immune cells to function, are attacked and their numbers fall. This weakens the body's fight against infection.

ENDOCRINE SYSTEM

THE BODY HAS TWO types of gland: exocrine glands, which secrete substances such as saliva through ducts, and ductless endocrine glands, which secrete hormones directly into the bloodstream. Hormones are chemical messengers that stimulate, regulate, and co-ordinate various processes and functions that occur within the body.

Hormones produced by the hypothalamus stimulate other glands to make and release their own hormones

The pineal gland produces melatonin that controls body rhythms, such as sleeping and waking

Known as the master gland, the pituitary gland helps to regulate hormone production in the body's other endocrine glands

The thyroid gland produces thyroxine, which controls growth, and calcitonin, which lowers blood calcium levels

The parathyroid glands make parathormone, which raises blood calcium levels

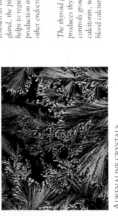

ADRENALINE CRYSTALS
Individual hormones can be crystallized and studied in a laboratory. Adrenaline hormone, secreted by the adrenal glands, works with the nervous system to prepare the body for fight or flight in stressful situations.

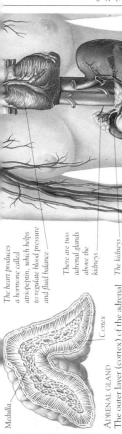

The heart produces a hormone called atriopeptin, which helps to regulate blood pressure and fluid balance

There are two adrenal glands above the kidneys

The kidneys produce erythropoietin, which acts on bone marrow to increase the production of red blood cells

The pancreas produces glucagon and insulin that regulate blood sugar levels

The stomach and intestines secrete hormones that aid digestion

The ovary makes female sex hormones, progestogen and oestrogen, which prepare the female body for reproduction

Medulla

Cortex

ADRENAL GLAND

The outer layer (cortex) of the adrenal gland produces hormones called corticosteroids, which help to control the metabolism (the body's chemical processes) and the concentration of salts in the blood. The inner medulla produces adrenaline.

ENDOCRINE FACTS
• Adrenaline gives superhuman strength in emergency situations.
• Too much growth hormone from the pituitary gland can produce gigantism (excessive growth).

73

The pituitary gland

Often referred to as the master gland, the pituitary is the most important endocrine gland. It produces its own hormones; these stimulate different endocrine glands to secrete other hormones. They also have a direct action on several body functions. The pituitary gland hangs down from part of the brain called the hypothalamus, which links the nervous and endocrine systems.

STRUCTURE

The pituitary gland is a pea-sized structure divided into two main parts: the anterior and posterior lobes. The anterior lobe makes its own hormones. The smaller, posterior lobe stores hormones that are made in the hypothalamus. There is also a tiny, intermediate lobe.

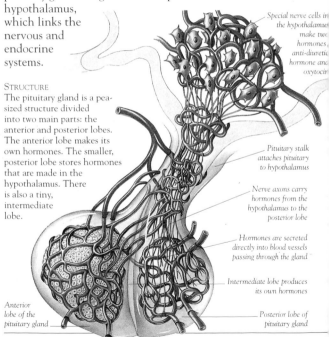

Special nerve cells in the hypothalamus make two hormones, anti-diuretic hormone and oxytocin

Pituitary stalk attaches pituitary to hypothalamus

Nerve axons carry hormones from the hypothalamus to the posterior lobe

Hormones are secreted directly into blood vessels passing through the gland

Intermediate lobe produces its own hormones

Anterior lobe of the pituitary gland

Posterior lobe of pituitary gland

EFFECTS OF SOME PITUITARY HORMONES

PITUITARY HORMONE	TARGET GLAND OR TISSUE	ACTION
ACTH Adrenocorticotropic hormone	ADRENAL GLAND	Stimulates the adrenal glands to produce steroid hormones. These regulate the metabolism of carbohydrates, fats, proteins, and minerals, and help the body adapt to stress.
Oxytocin and prolactin hormones	UTERINE MUSCLES AND MAMMARY GLANDS	These stimulate the breasts so that milk is produced after pregnancy for as long as the baby continues to feed. Oxytocin also stimulates the contraction of the uterus during childbirth.
TSH Thyroid-stimulating hormone	THYROID GLAND	Triggers production of hormones in the thyroid gland. These regulate the metabolic rate and growth. They also have an effect on the heart rate.
FSH AND LH Follicle-stimulating hormone and leuteinizing hormone	TESTIS AND OVARY	Both these pituitary hormones act on the sex glands (ovaries or testes) to stimulate the production of sex hormones. These glands control sexual development and the release of eggs or sperm.
ADH Anti-diuretic hormone (also known as vasopressin)	KIDNEY TUBULES	Has a direct action on the kidney to control the amount of water lost in the urine. ADH also causes small arteries to constrict when blood pressure is low.
MSH Melanocyte-stimulating hormone	SKIN	Has a direct action on pigment cells in the skin (melanocytes) to trigger the production of the tanning pigment, melanin, which provides some protection against the harmful effects of the sun's rays.
GH Growth hormone	BONE AND GENERAL GROWTH	Acts on the whole body to promote growth by stimulating the division of cells. It is vital for normal growth and development in children.

RESPIRATORY SYSTEM

A REGULAR SUPPLY of oxygen from the air is vital to life. Air enters the body through the nose and mouth, where it is filtered. It then passes down through the trachea (windpipe) into the lungs. The trachea has two main branches, the left and right bronchi, which divide into a network of smaller bronchioles. These lead into clusters of tiny air spaces, called alveoli.

THE LUNGS LIE IN THE MIDDLE OF THE CHEST

LARYNX

Made of cartilage, the larynx links the base of the throat to the trachea. A protective flap, the epiglottis, and the false vocal cords close the larynx to stop food going down the wrong way during swallowing.

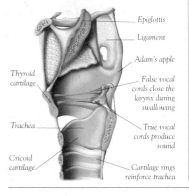

Thyroid cartilage

Trachea

Cricoid cartilage

Epiglottis

Ligament

Adam's apple

False vocal cords close the larynx during swallowing

True vocal cords produce sound

Cartilage rings reinforce trachea

OPEN

The vocal cords are open when at rest

CLOSED

Air passing through closed cords produces sound

VOCAL CORDS

As air passes through the pair of fibrous vocal cords, they vibrate and make sounds. These are modulated by the mouth and tongue to produce speech. High-pitched sounds are made by tightening the cords. Deep sounds are made by loosening the vocal cords.

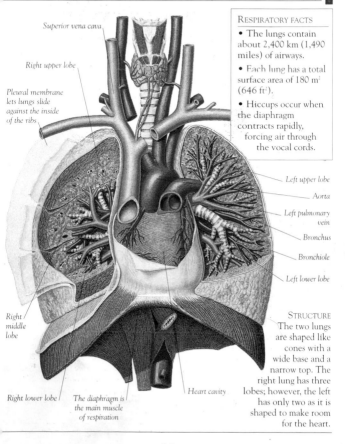

Superior vena cava

Right upper lobe

Pleural membrane
lets lungs slide
against the inside
of the ribs

Right middle lobe

Right lower lobe

The diaphragm is
the main muscle
of respiration

Heart cavity

Left upper lobe

Aorta

Left pulmonary vein

Bronchus

Bronchiole

Left lower lobe

RESPIRATORY FACTS

• The lungs contain about 2,400 km (1,490 miles) of airways.

• Each lung has a total surface area of 180 m² (646 ft²).

• Hiccups occur when the diaphragm contracts rapidly, forcing air through the vocal cords.

STRUCTURE

The two lungs are shaped like cones with a wide base and a narrow top. The right lung has three lobes; however, the left has only two as it is shaped to make room for the heart.

Lung functions

Air is drawn in and out of the lungs by the contraction and relaxation of the diaphragm muscle. Once air reaches the lungs, oxygen is extracted and passes into the blood through the thin walls of microscopic air sacs (alveoli). It is exchanged for the body's waste product, carbon dioxide, which is exhaled (breathed out).

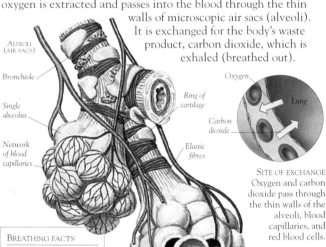

ALVEOLI (AIR SACS)

Bronchiole

Single alveolus

Network of blood capillaries

Ring of cartilage

Elastic fibres

Oxygen

Carbon dioxide

Lung

SITE OF EXCHANGE
Oxygen and carbon dioxide pass through the thin walls of the alveoli, blood capillaries, and red blood cells.

ALVEOLI
Oxygen passes from the alveoli into a surrounding network of capillaries. It binds with haemoglobin in red blood cells. Carbon dioxide gas passes in the other direction from the blood to the alveoli for exhalation.

Grape-like clusters of alveoli

BREATHING FACTS

• The lungs contain over 300 million alveoli.

• Every minute, about 6 litres (10.5 pints) of air is breathed in.

• Adult lungs hold an average of 3 litres (5 pints) of air.

BREATHING IN

Lungs expand, drawing in air

Intercostal muscles contract

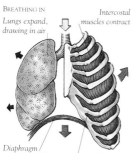

Diaphragm contracts and flattens

Ribs lift upwards and outwards

INHALATION

When the diaphragm contracts and the rib cage expands, pressure in the chest cavity lowers and air rushes into the lungs.

BREATHING OUT

Lungs contract, forcing air out

Intercostal muscles relax

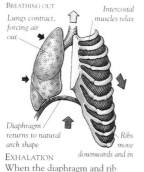

Diaphragm returns to natural arch shape

Ribs move downwards and in

EXHALATION

When the diaphragm and rib cage relax, pressure in the chest increases, forcing air out again.

AIR COMPOSITION

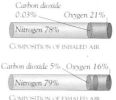

Carbon dioxide 0.03% — *Oxygen 21%*

Nitrogen 78%

COMPOSITION OF INHALED AIR

Carbon dioxide 5% — *Oxygen 16%*

Nitrogen 79%

COMPOSITION OF EXHALED AIR

AIR Mouth-to-mouth resuscitation uses the oxygen in exhaled air to revive a person who has stopped breathing.

SMOKING

Cigarette smoke irritates the lungs and enters the bloodstream. Linked with 90 per cent of all cancers, smoking also increases the risk of high blood pressure, strokes, and other circulatory problems.

SMOKE DEPOSITS IN LUNG

COMMON RESPIRATORY PROBLEMS	
NAME	DESCRIPTION
Asthma	Constricted bronchioles trigger coughing, wheezing, and breathlessness.
Acute bronchitis	Temporary inflammation of bronchi due to infection.
Chronic bronchitis	Long-term inflammation of airways due to smoking or pollution.
Emphysema	Breakdown of alveolar structure, often due to smoking, causes breathlessness.
Pneumonia	Alveoli fill with fluid and dead white blood cells due to bacterial infection.

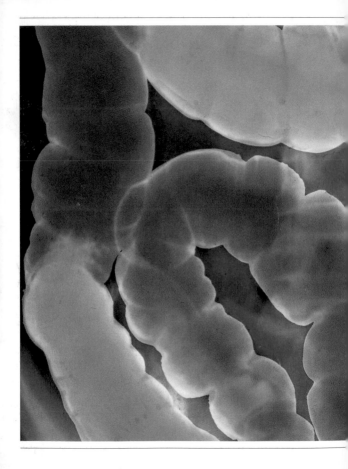

DIGESTION AND EXCRETION

DIGESTIVE SYSTEM

FOOD MUST be broken down into its basic components before the body can absorb and use its nutrients. This process of digestion starts with the mouth watering. As food passes through the body, it is broken down by enzymes – special proteins that accelerate the body's chemical reactions. Undigested waste is excreted as faeces.

Epiglottis stops fluid entering the trachea during swallowing

Food is broken down in the mouth by chewing

Salivary glands add enzymes that break down starch

Food is swallowed as a lump called a bolus

Waves of muscular action carry food down the oesophagus into the stomach

Food is churned, digested, and stored in the stomach

The liver makes bile that helps to break fat into tiny globules

The gallbladder stores bile until it is needed

The pancreas releases digestive enzymes that break down starch, fat, and protein

The small intestine is the main site for the absorption of minerals and other nutrients

In the colon, water is absorbed and bowel contents solidify

The appendix has no known function in humans

The rectum is a muscular tube that expels digestive waste through the anus

DIGESTIVE ROUTE

The digestive tract runs from the mouth to the anus and is about 9 m (30 ft) long. Food passes from the mouth, down the oesophagus into the stomach. From here, it passes into the small intestine made up of the duodenum, jejunum, and ileum, and into the large intestine, made up of the colon and rectum. Several organs and glands are connected to the tract to help digestion.

FOOD BREAK-DOWN

REGION/GLAND	SECRET ON	ENZYME PRODUCED	FOOD ACTED ON	PRODUCT
Salivary glands (mouth)	Saliva	Amylase	Starch	Maltose
Gastric glands (stomach)	Gastric juices	Pepsin, lipase	Proteins, fats	Amino acids and fatty acids
Pancreas	Pancreatic juices	Trypsin, elastase, lipase, amylase	Proteins, fats, starch	Amino acids, fatty acids, maltose
Small intestine	Succus entericus	Sucrase, lactase, peptidase, lipase	Sucrose, lactose, proteins, fats	Galactose, amino and fatty acids
Colon (large intestine)	Bacterial secretions	Bacterial enzymes	Undigested vegetable fibre	Gases and fermentation products

MOUTH AND TEETH

USED FOR MANY FUNCTIONS, including breathing and talking, the mouth is the entrance of the digestive tract. During eating, teeth cut and grind food to break it down. After saliva has lubricated the food, the tongue rolls it into a ball (bolus) and pushes it to the back of the mouth, ready for swallowing.

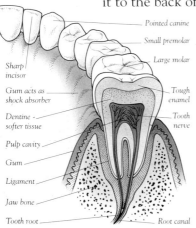

Pointed canine

Small premolar

Large molar

Sharp incisor

Gum acts as shock absorber

Dentine - softer tissue

Pulp cavity

Gum

Ligament

Jaw bone

Tough enamel

Tooth nerve

Tooth root

Root canal

THE TEETH

There are three types of teeth: incisors have sharp edges for cutting; canines have pointed tips for tearing; and molars have flattened, ridged surfaces for grinding. Teeth are coated in enamel, the hardest substance in the body. Beneath this is a softer layer of dentine.

TEETH AT BIRTH (MILK TEETH IN GREY)

TEETH AT THREE YEARS (ADULT TEETH IN BLUE)

TEETH AT NINE YEARS

GROWTH

All teeth are present at birth as tiny buds deep in the jawbone. The 20 milk teeth usually appear between the ages of six months and three years. The 32 adult teeth usually appear between the ages of six and 20 years.

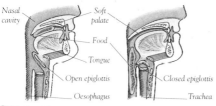

Nasal cavity
Soft palate
Food
Tongue
Open epiglottis
Oesophagus
Closed epiglottis
Trachea

SWALLOWING

When food reaches the back of the mouth, it triggers the swallowing reflex. An automatic wave of muscle contraction propels food through the oesophagus, a muscular tube that leads to the stomach.

MOUTH FACTS

• Some people never develop the back four molars (wisdom teeth).

• Acids, secreted by bacteria in the mouth to break down sugars, cause tooth decay.

• An adult secretes about 1 litre (1 6 pints) of saliva a day.

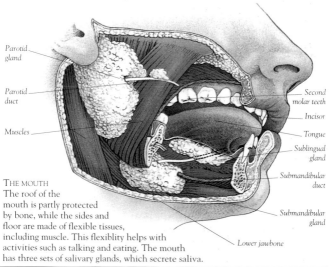

Parotid gland
Parotid duct
Muscles
Second molar teeth
Incisor
Tongue
Sublingual gland
Submandibular duct
Submandibular gland
Lower jawbone

THE MOUTH

The roof of the mouth is partly protected by bone, while the sides and floor are made of flexible tissues, including muscle. This flexiblity helps with activities such as talking and eating. The mouth has three sets of salivary glands, which secrete saliva.

THE STOMACH

WHEN FOOD IS SWALLOWED, it passes down the oesophagus into the stomach, which lies high on the left side of the abdominal cavity. Semi-digested food leaves the stomach through a muscular ring (pyloric sphincter) and enters the intestines.

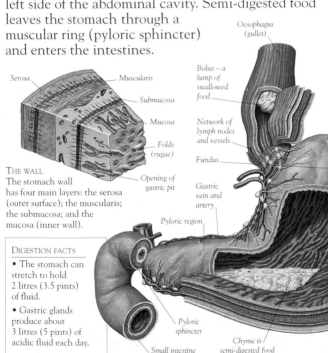

Serosa

Muscularis

Submucosa

Mucosa

Folds (rugae)

Opening of gastric pit

Oesophagus (gullet)

Bolus – a lump of swallowed food

Network of lymph nodes and vessels

Fundus

Gastric vein and artery

Pyloric region

Pyloric sphincter

Small intestine

Chyme is semi-digested food

THE WALL
The stomach wall has four main layers: the serosa (outer surface); the muscularis; the submucosa; and the mucosa (inner wall).

DIGESTION FACTS

• The stomach can stretch to hold 2 litres (3.5 pints) of fluid.

• Gastric glands produce about 3 litres (5 pints) of acidic fluid each day.

GASTRIC PITS
Glands in the gastric pits secrete hydrochloric acid and powerful enzymes. These break up complex food molecules into simpler chemicals. The stomach does not digest itself because it is protected by a mucus lining.

The mucosa has deep folds called rugae, which flatten out when the stomach is full

The muscularis contains 3 muscle layers – oblique, circular, and longitudinal

Serosa

STRUCTURE
The stomach, a hollow J-shaped sac, is the most elastic part of the body. Its upper pole, the fundus, is the widest part, and its narrow exit is in the pyloric region.

FILLING AND EMPTYING

ACTION
Food spends about six hours in the stomach. The muscular wall churns up food ready for digestion. Semi-digested food forms a slurry called chyme.

As food enters, the stomach stretches

More gastric juices are produced

Stomach churning increases and, within a few hours, its contents form chyme

Wave-like muscle contractions push chyme downwards

The pyloric sphincter relaxes to let some chyme through

The stomach gradually shrinks as chyme passes into the duodenum

PYLORIC SPHINCTER

PYLORIC SPHINCTER
This muscular, ring-like thickening of the intestine wall is usually closed to keep the stomach full. It relaxes for a few seconds to let chyme squirt into the intestines.

THE INTESTINES

COILED INSIDE the abdominal cavity is the intestinal tube. In the small intestine, nutrients are absorbed and enzymes complete the digestive process. In the large intestine (bowel), wastes are solidified.

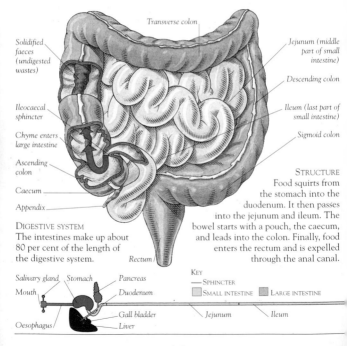

Transverse colon

Solidified faeces (undigested wastes)

Ileocaecal sphincter

Chyme enters large intestine

Ascending colon

Caecum

Appendix

Jejunum (middle part of small intestine)

Descending colon

Ileum (last part of small intestine)

Sigmoid colon

Rectum

DIGESTIVE SYSTEM
The intestines make up about 80 per cent of the length of the digestive system.

Salivary gland   Stomach   Pancreas

Mouth

Duodenum

Oesophagus

Gall bladder

Liver

STRUCTURE
Food squirts from the stomach into the duodenum. It then passes into the jejunum and ileum. The bowel starts with a pouch, the caecum, and leads into the colon. Finally, food enters the rectum and is expelled through the anal canal.

KEY
— SPHINCTER
☐ SMALL INTESTINE   ☐ LARGE INTESTINE

Jejunum   Ileum

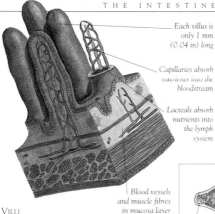

Each villus is only 1 mm (0.04 in) long

Capillaries absorb nutrients into the bloodstream

Lacteals absorb nutrients into the lymph system

Blood vessels and muscle fibres in mucosa layer

VILLI
The intestinal wall is covered in tiny projections, called villi. These absorb nutrients from the intestines into the blood capillaries and lymph vessels, called lacteals.

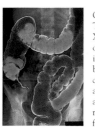

COLON X-RAY
This false-colour X-ray shows part of the large intestine. Here, bacteria break down some fibres and excess water is absorbed. Waste remains soldify to form faeces.

Intestine

Muscle contracts behind food

Food

Food slides forward

Muscles in front of food relax

Contractions push food along the digestive tract

PERISTALSIS
The wall of the digestive tract contains longitudinal and circular muscle fibres. These produce wave-like contractions called peristalsis, propelling food through the intestines.

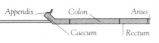

Appendix   Colon   Anus

Caecum   Rectum

LIVER AND PANCREAS

TWO IMPORTANT ORGANS are closely associated with the intestines: the liver and the pancreas. The liver secretes bile, a digestive juice that breaks down fats and processes nutrients, carried to it from the stomach and intestines by the portal vein. Pancreatic enzymes enter the duodenum to aid digestion.

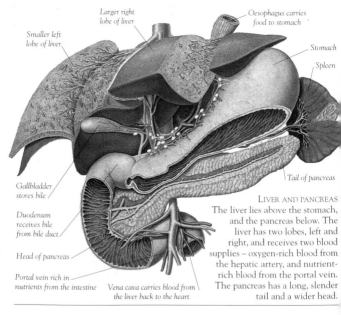

Larger right lobe of liver

Oesophagus carries food to stomach

Smaller left lobe of liver

Stomach

Spleen

Tail of pancreas

Gallbladder stores bile

Duodenum receives bile from bile duct

Head of pancreas

Portal vein rich in nutrients from the intestine

Vena cava carries blood from the liver back to the heart

LIVER AND PANCREAS
The liver lies above the stomach, and the pancreas below. The liver has two lobes, left and right, and receives two blood supplies – oxygen-rich blood from the hepatic artery, and nutrient-rich blood from the portal vein. The pancreas has a long, slender tail and a wider head.

LIVER FUNCTIONS

The liver performs many vital functions. It stores chemicals and carries out many different chemical processes.

- Makes bile for digesting food.
- Breaks down fats and excess amino acids (units of protein).
- Helps maintain blood sugar levels.
- Stores fat-soluble vitamins and some minerals (e.g. iron and copper).
- Makes heat to warm passing blood.
- Makes blood proteins.
- Helps clot blood.
- Controls blood cell formation and destruction.
- Removes poisonous chemicals from the blood, and breaks them down.

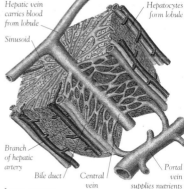

Hepatic vein carries blood from lobule

Hepatocytes form lobule

Sinusoid

Branch of hepatic artery

Bile duct

Central vein

Portal vein supplies nutrients

LIVER LOBULE

Billions of liver cells (hepatocytes) are arranged into thousands of six-sided columns called lobules. Blood flows from both the hepatic artery and portal vein into spaces (sinusoids) to supply oxygen and nutrients to the hepatocytes.

Exocrine glands make digestive enzymes

Ducts carry digestive juices

Endocrine glands secrete hormones into bloodstream

PANCREAS

Some pancreatic cells form clusters of exocrine glands that secrete digestive enzymes. Other pancreatic cells form endocrine glands. These secrete hormones (insulin and glucagon) that help to regulate blood sugar.

GALL BLADDER

When semi-digested food enters the duodenum, the gallbladder contracts to pump bile through the bile duct into the intestines.

URINARY SYSTEM

EXCESS FLUID AND SOLUBLE substances
are removed from the blood circulation by
the kidneys. Some fluid and nutrients are
reabsorbed back into the bloodstream, while
excess water and waste products are expelled
from the body as urine.

LOCATION OF
URINARY
SYSTEM

*Renal vein
takes away
filtered blood*

*Urine-collecting
areas (calyces)
channel urine
into the ureter*

*Adrenal
gland*

*Renal artery
brings in blood
for filtering*

*Urine-collecting
tube in medulla*

Arteriole

*Capillary
network*

Cortex

Medulla

*Ureter drains
urine from
kidney to bladder*

Venule

*Knot of
capillaries
(glomerulus)
in cortex*

SECTION OF THE KIDNEY
There are over a million
filtration units (nephrons); this
network of tubules loops down
from the cortex to the medulla.

KIDNEYS
The two kidneys are bean-shaped
organs at the back of the abdomen.
They regulate body-fluid and salt levels
and help to control blood acidity. Each
kidney is about 12 cm (5 in) long and
contains two layers of tissue: an outer
cortex and an inner medulla.

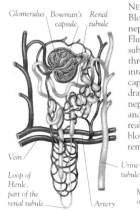

Glomerulus Bowman's Renal
capsule tubule

Vein

Loop of
Henle,
part of the
renal tubule

Urine-collecting
tubule

Artery

NEPHRON

Blood flows into the nephron under pressure. Fluid and soluble substances filter through the capillaries into the Bowman's capsule. As filtered fluid drains down the nephron, most water and nutrients are reabsorbed by the blood. Only urine remains in the nephron.

KIDNEY FACTS

• Every hour, the kidneys filter up to 7 litres (12 pints) of fluid from the blood.

• Urine is 95% water.

• Urine contains poisonous substances including urea, made in the liver.

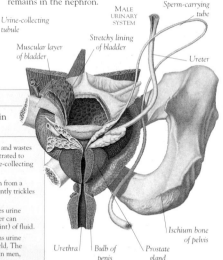

MALE
URINARY
SYSTEM

Sperm-carrying
tube

Muscular layer
of bladder

Stretchy lining
of bladder

Ureter

Ischium bone
of pelvis

Urethra Bulb of
penis

Prostate
gland

URINARY SYSTEM

There are four main stages in the urinary system:

• Kidneys – two organs where fluid and wastes are filtered from blood and concentrated to form urine. This trickles down urine-collecting ducts into the ureters.

• Ureters – two tubes that each run from a kidney to the bladder. Urine constantly trickles down these, day and night.

• Bladder – an elastic sac that stores urine until it can be expelled. The bladder can stretch to hold over half a litre (1 pint) of fluid.

• Urethra – a single tube that drains urine from the bladder to the outside world. The urethra is about 20 cm (8 in) long in men, but only 4 cm (1.5 in) long in women.

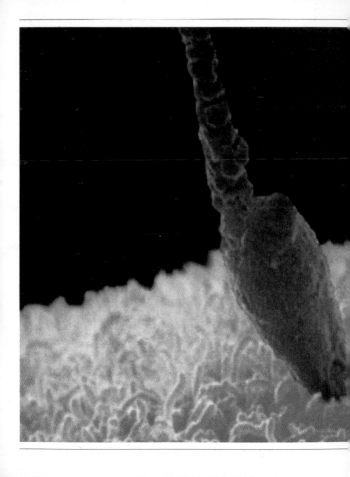

REPRODUCTION

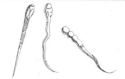

REPRODUCTIVE SYSTEMS

FOR THE HUMAN RACE to continue, people need to reproduce. From the early teens, the male and female reproductive systems produce sex cells. These unite through sexual reproduction to form a new life.

Male reproductive system

The male sex glands are called testes (testicles). These produce mobile sex cells (spermatozoa or sperm). These pass through two tubes, the vas deferens and the epididymis, to reach the penis. Glands, such as the prostate and seminal vesicles, secrete fluids that nourish the sperm.

LOCATION OF MALE REPRODUCTIVE SYSTEM

STRUCTURE

The main organs of the male reproductive system, the testes and the penis, are outside the abdomen. The prostate gland is wrapped around the urethra between the bladder and the penis. The penis acts as an outlet for both the urinary and reproductive systems.

Vena cava

Aorta

Right leg

Bladder

Ligament suspends penis from pubic bone

Prostate gland

Urethra

Penis contains spongy tissue

Scrotum contains two testes

Spermatic cord

SPERM CELLS

Between an oval head and a whip-like tail is a middle piece, packed with energy-releasing structures called mitochondria. These help the tail propel the sperm along the female reproductive tract. A healthy adult male produces about 500 million sperm a day.

Head contains a nucleus

Middle piece

Tail

SPERM

Colon

MALE REPRODUCTION

• A sperm is 0.05 mm (0.002 in) long.

• A sperm takes about 10 weeks to mature.

• Each testis produces about 1,500 sperm per second.

• Sperm swim at a rate of about 3 mm (0.08 in) per hour.

TESTES

Hanging outside the body, the testes are kept a few degrees cooler than the rest of the abdomen. This is vital for sperm production. The testes also produce testosterone, the hormone that controls male development.

Vas deferens stores sperm

Testicular veins and artery

Head of coiled epididymis

Seminiferous tubules

3 layers of protective tissue

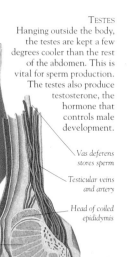

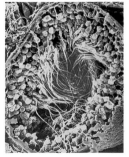

CROSS-SECTION OF TESTIS

DEVELOPING SPERM

The testes contain about 1,000 seminiferous tubules where sperm are produced. They are nourished by special cells, before passing into the tightly coiled epididymis to mature. Here, they are stored until needed.

Female reproductive system

The female sex glands are the ovaries. These produce sex cells called ova (eggs). Usually one egg is released every 28 days during the menstrual cycle. It passes down one of two Fallopian tubes into the uterus (womb). If the egg is fertilized by a sperm, it becomes embedded in the womb lining. Otherwise the egg and lining are shed in a menstrual period.

LOCATION OF FEMALE
REPRODUCTIVE SYSTEM

STRUCTURE

The female organs lie in the pelvis. At the lower end of the uterus (womb), a narrow opening (cervix) leads into the vagina. At the top end, two openings lead into the Fallopian tubes. These widen out to embrace the ovaries and trap released eggs.

Ovarian ligament

Uterus has thick wall

Ovary

The Fallopian tube sweeps the released egg down towards the uterus

During the menstrual cycle, several eggs start to ripen, producing bulges on the ovary surface. Usually only one egg is released

The vagina has a muscular wall that stretches during childbirth

The womb lining plumps up each month, ready to receive the fertilized egg

UTERUS

Normally about the size of a fist, the uterus is a pear-shaped organ with a thick, muscular wall. During pregnancy it can expand over a 1,000 times in volume to hold a developing baby.

THE OVUM (EGG)

In the ovary, ova ripen in fluid-filled follicles. Once a month, one follicle outgrows the others and bursts, releasing its egg. An ovum is surrounded by follicle cells and a membrane (zona pellucida).

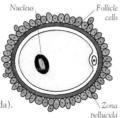

Nucleus — *Follicle cells*

Zona pellucida

FEMALE REPRODUCTION

• Non-identical twins result, if two eggs are fertilized in one cycle.

• The diameter of the ovum is 0.1–0.2 mm (0.003–0.008 in), which is 50 times wider than a sperm head.

THE MENSTRUAL CYCLE

The menstrual cycle is controlled by the pituitary gland. This produces hormones that stimulate the ovaries to produce oestrogen and progesterone, and trigger the release of an egg. At the same time, the womb lining undergoes cyclical changes.

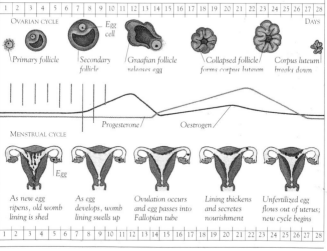

| 1 | 2 | 3 | 4 | 5 | 6 | 7 | 8 | 9 | 10 | 11 | 12 | 13 | 14 | 15 | 16 | 17 | 18 | 19 | 20 | 21 | 22 | 23 | 24 | 25 | 26 | 27 | 28 |

OVARIAN CYCLE

DAYS

Egg cell

Primary follicle *Secondary follicle* *Graafian follicle releases egg* *Collapsed follicle forms corpus luteum* *Corpus luteum breaks down*

Progesterone   *Oestrogen*

MENSTRUAL CYCLE

Egg

As new egg ripens, old womb lining is shed

As egg develops, womb lining swells up

Ovulation occurs and egg passes into Fallopian tube

Lining thickens and secretes nourishment

Unfertilized egg flows out of uterus; new cycle begins

| 1 | 2 | 3 | 4 | 5 | 6 | 7 | 8 | 9 | 10 | 11 | 12 | 13 | 14 | 15 | 16 | 17 | 18 | 19 | 20 | 21 | 22 | 23 | 24 | 25 | 26 | 27 | 28 |

SEX AND FERTILIZATION

SPERM CELLS ENTER the female's body during sexual intercourse; if a sperm fertilizes an egg, new life begins. The sperm and the ovum contain genetic material, which is joined through sexual reproduction to provide instructions for the development of the baby.

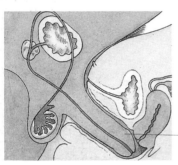

SEXUAL INTERCOURSE
The male's penis fills with blood and becomes hard and erect. It is inserted into the woman's vagina. Sexual intercourse can produce pleasurable sensations for both partners. In the male, reflex contractions suddenly release (ejaculate) a fluid (semen) containing sperm into the woman's vagina.

The penis is placed inside the vagina

Millions of sperm race towards the ripe egg

FERTILIZATION FACTS

• A newly released egg must be fertilized within 24–48 hours.

• A baby is usually born about 40 weeks after fertilization.

• Sometimes a newly fertilized egg splits to produce identical twins.

SPERM RACE
A man's semen usually contains about 300 million sperm. These swim in search of an egg. Only 50–150 sperm reach the egg as it travels down a Fallopian tube. Of these, only one will fertilize the egg.

SPERM SWIMMING IN SEMEN

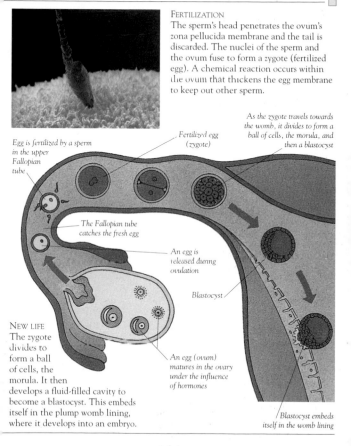

FERTILIZATION

The sperm's head penetrates the ovum's zona pellucida membrane and the tail is discarded. The nuclei of the sperm and the ovum fuse to form a zygote (fertilized egg). A chemical reaction occurs within the ovum that thickens the egg membrane to keep out other sperm.

As the zygote travels towards the womb, it divides to form a ball of cells, the morula, and then a blastocyst

Fertilized egg (zygote)

Egg is fertilized by a sperm in the upper Fallopian tube

The Fallopian tube catches the fresh egg

An egg is released during ovulation

Blastocyst

NEW LIFE

The zygote divides to form a ball of cells, the morula. It then develops a fluid-filled cavity to become a blastocyst. This embeds itself in the plump womb lining, where it develops into an embryo.

An egg (ovum) matures in the ovary under the influence of hormones

Blastocyst embeds itself in the womb lining

PREGNANCY AND BIRTH

DURING THE FIRST EIGHT weeks of pregnancy, while
the internal organs are developing, the baby is called
an embryo. Once movement
begins and the organs have
formed, it is known as a
fetus. Growth is then rapid.

8 WEEKS
The fetus is
protected by
amniotic fluid
and is nourished
through the
umbilical cord.

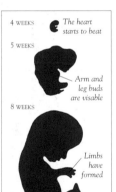

4 WEEKS ● *The heart
starts to beat*

5 WEEKS

*Arm and
leg buds
are visable*

8 WEEKS

*Limbs
have
formed*

*Length: 2.5 cm
(1 in)
Weight: 2 g
(0.07 oz)*

12 WEEKS
The head is large
compared with the
body. Tiny nails grow
on the fingers and toes.
The eyes are closed.
32 permanent teeth
buds develop.

*Length: 16 cm (6 in)
Weight: 140 g
(5 oz)*

*Length: 7.5 cm (3 in)
Weight: 18 g
(0.6 oz)*

THE EMBRYO
These pictures show the
actual size of an embryo
as it becomes recognizably
human in shape.

16 WEEKS
The fetus is covered
in fine, downy hair.
External genitals are
visible. Movements
can sometimes be
felt from 16 weeks.

*Placenta supplies fetus with
nutrients and oxygen, and
removes fetal wastes*

FETUS AT FOUR MONTHS

THE FETUS
The umbilical cord connects the fetus to the placenta, a spongy organ attached to the womb lining. By 16 weeks, the facial features are well formed and blood vessels are visible under the paper-thin skin.

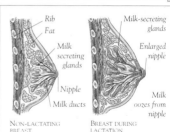

NON-LACTATING BREAST

BREAST DURING LACTATION

Rib

Fat

Milk secreting glands

Nipple

Milk ducts

Milk-secreting glands

Enlarged nipple

Milk oozes from nipple

LACTATION
During pregnancy, the breasts enlarge, and milk glands develop. Breast milk provides nourishment and protective antibodies for the newborn child.

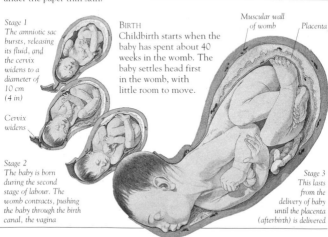

Stage 1
The amniotic sac bursts, releasing its fluid, and the cervix widens to a diameter of 10 cm (4 in)

Cervix widens

Stage 2
The baby is born during the second stage of labour. The womb contracts, pushing the baby through the birth canal, the vagina

BIRTH
Childbirth starts when the baby has spent about 40 weeks in the womb. The baby settles head first in the womb, with little room to move.

Muscular wall of womb

Placenta

Stage 3
This lasts from the delivery of baby until the placenta (afterbirth) is delivered

GENETICS AND HEREDITY

FOUND IN THE NUCLEUS of each cell are structures called chromosomes. These contain molecules of deoxyribonucleic acid (DNA), which are made up of strings of genes. Each gene unit contains the information needed to make a single protein used to build and control cells. Genes decide a person's characteristics, such as hair and eye colour. During sexual reproduction, sex cells pass genes onto the next generation.

GENETICS FACTS
• Sperm have an X or a Y chromosome that determines a baby's sex.
• The majority of body cells contain 46 chromosomes.
• Red blood cells have no nucleus and so do not carry genes.

DNA IN CELL
NUCLEUS

DNA molecule unwinds to copy information from gene

Information from a gene is used to make a single protein

Each chain contains a series of nucleic acid bases that code genetic information

GENES

A chromosome contains a tightly wound spiral of DNA. This complex chemical structure unwinds to expose genes when they are needed. Genes make the proteins required for the production of new cells. Before a cell divides, the chromosome makes a copy of itself.

A chromosome has two identical arms called chromatids

DNA molecule is made up of two strands

Each cell has 46 chromosomes in its nucleus

Cell

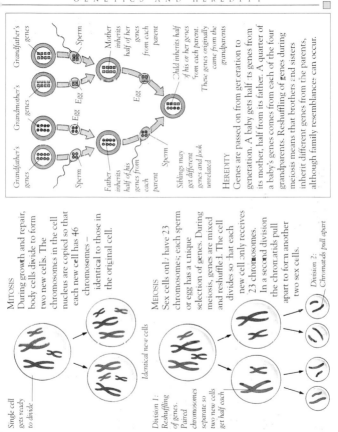

Grandfather's genes

Grandmother's genes

Grandfather's genes

Sperm

Egg   Egg

Egg

Mother inherits half of her genes from each parent

Child inherits half of his or her genes from each parent. These genes originally came from the grandparents

Grandfather's genes

Sperm

Sperm

Father inherits half of his genes from each parent

Sperm

Siblings may get different genes and look unrelated

HEREDITY

Genes are passed on from generation to generation. A baby gets half its genes from its mother, half from its father. A quarter of a baby's genes comes from each of the four grandparents. Reshuffling of genes during meiosis means that brothers and sisters inherit different genes from the parents, although family resemblances can occur.

MITOSIS

During growth and repair, body cells divide to form two new cells. The chromosomes in the cell nucleus are copied so that each new cell has 46 chromosomes – identical to those in the original cell.

Single cell gets ready to divide

Identical new cells

MEIOSIS

Sex cells only have 23 chromosomes; each sperm or egg has a unique selection of genes. During meiosis, genes are mixed and reshuffled. The cell divides so that each new cell only receives 23 chromosomes.

In a second division the chromatids pull apart to form another two sex cells.

Division 1: Reshuffling of genes. Paired chromosomes separate so two new cells get half each

Division 2: Chromatids pull apart

105

GROWING UP

GROWTH IS RAPID during the first few years of life, when children learn to walk and talk. It steadies during childhood, and then speeds up again at puberty, when psychological and physical changes occur that make reproduction possible. By the late teens, growth stops and adulthood begins.

HELPLESS BABY
A newborn baby can hear well but cannot see properly. It may spend at least 12 hours each day asleep. The only way a baby can show fear, discomfort, pain, hunger, or boredom is by crying.

BODY PROPORTIONS
During growth and development, physical proportions change dramatically so that the head becomes smaller in relation to the body.

• A baby's head is about a quarter of total body length.

• During childhood, the relative size of the head and trunk decreases while the legs and arms become proportionately longer.

• An adult's head is about an eighth of total body length.

• A newborn baby can grow from a length of about 51 cm (20 in) to an eventual height of 180 cm (6 ft) or more.

2 MONTHS: 55 CM
(1FT 10 IN)

2 YEARS: 86 CM
(2FT 10 IN)

CHILD DEVELOPMENT

6 MONTHS
Babies can sit
up if supported
and control the
weight
of their head.

18 MONTHS
Children can walk
unaided, climb
stairs, and
know at least
six words.

9–12 MONTHS
Most babies can crawl
and pull themselves
upright. They may
be able
to stand
without
support.

2–3 YEAR OLDS
Children can
hold a pencil,
scribble, and copy
simple shapes.
They talk in
simple sentences.

PUBERTY FACTS

• During puberty,
people become sexually
mature; eggs or sperm
start being produced.

• Puberty is triggered
by hormones released
from the brain.

• In girls, puberty starts
between the ages of
9–13. In boys, puberty
starts later, between
the ages of 10–14.

• Hormonal changes
at puberty often cause
greasy skin and acne.

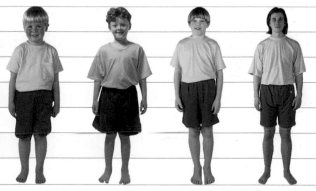

4 YEARS: 112 CM
(3 FT 8 IN)

7 YEARS: 122 CM
(4 FT)

12 YEARS: 147 CM
(4 FT 10 IN)

20 YEARS: 178 CM
(5 FT 10 IN)

GROWING OLD

AS PEOPLE GROW OLDER, their body cells gradually deteriorate. This results in physical changes such as brittle bones. Medical advances have increased the average life span, lengthening the aging period. A good diet and regular exercise can delay the signs of aging.

AGING

Typical signs of aging include wrinkles and grey or white hair. Wrinkles first appear on the forehead, where skin is creased from smiling and frowning.

EFFECTS OF AGE ON THE REPRODUCTIVE SYSTEMS
Men make sperm and remain fertile from puberty throughout the rest of their lives. Women run out of eggs at an average age of 51 years, when they go through menopause. The ovarian and menstrual cycles cease; at this time a woman is no longer naturally fertile.

MEN
• From the age of 45, a man's prostate gland naturally enlarges and may interfere with his urine flow.   • Men can still father a child at the age of 90 or older.

WOMEN
• Many women suffer menopausal symptoms such as hot flushes, sweating, and mood changes when the ovaries stop making the hormone oestrogen.   • Lack of oestrogen can trigger brittleness in bones and quicken the hardening of the arteries. Hormone replacement therapy can help to prevent these problems and relieve menopausal symptoms.

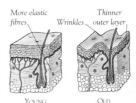

More elastic fibres

Wrinkles

Thinner outer layer

YOUNG SKIN

OLD SKIN

SKIN

With age, skin becomes tougher, less elastic, and wrinkly. The cell of the outer layer are renewed les often, and the deeper layers lose many of their supporting tissues.

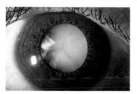

CATARACT

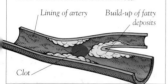

An operation can remove a cataract

CATARACT

The aging lens can develop a cataract; the crystal-clear lens becomes cloudy and opaque, and light rays are blocked.

VISION

As people grow older, the lens of the eye often stiffens and cannot focus on nearby objects. This causes long-sightedness. The retina's macula, where fine detail is picked out, may degenerate so that eyesight begins to fail.

Lens loses elasticity and cannot focus

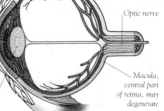

Optic nerve

Macula, central part of retina, may degenerate

ARTERIES

Aging arteries lose their elasticity. Damage due to smoking, high blood pressure, or eating excess fat causes arteries to harden and clog up with fatty deposits. Blood clots may form and block the circulation.

Lining of artery   Build-up of fatty deposits

Clot

COMMON CAUSES OF DEATH

The elderly often die peacefully in their sleep, when their heart stops beating.

CAUSE	WHAT HAPPENS?
Heart attack	Heart stops beating due to poor blood supply and lack of oxygen.
Stroke	Brain cells die suddenly due to blockage of a major blood vessel.
Cancer	Uncontrollable growth of abnormal cells causes weakness.
Broncho-pneumonia	Overwhelming airway infection interferes with breathing.
Accident	Injury to a vital organ or loss of blood produces collapse.

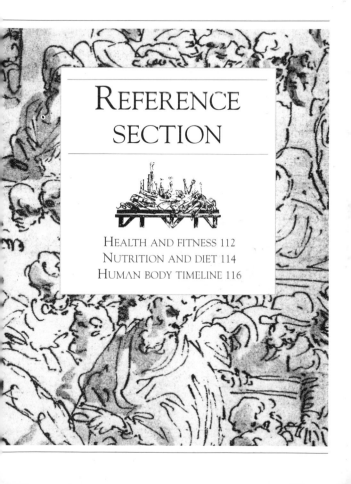

REFERENCE
SECTION

HEALTH AND FITNESS

REGULAR EXERCISE will help to keep you fit and healthy. People who exercise at least 20–30 minutes three times per week, lower their risk of becoming overweight and suffering from high blood pressure, a stroke, or coronary heart disease. Ideally, you should take some form of exercise every day.

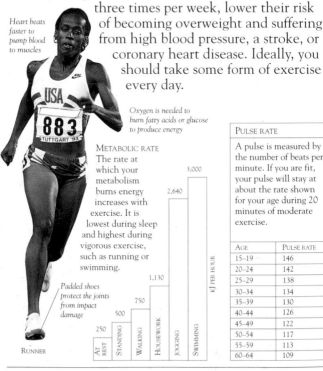

Heart beats faster to pump blood to muscles

Oxygen is needed to burn fatty acids or glucose to produce energy

METABOLIC RATE
The rate at which your metabolism burns energy increases with exercise. It is lowest during sleep and highest during vigorous exercise, such as running or swimming.

Padded shoes protect the joints from impact damage

RUNNER

	KJ PER HOUR
AT REST	250
STANDING	500
WALKING	750
HOUSEWORK	1,130
JOGGING	2,640
SWIMMING	3,000

PULSE RATE

A pulse is measured by the number of beats per minute. If you are fit, your pulse will stay at about the rate shown for your age during 20 minutes of moderate exercise.

AGE	PULSE RATE
15–19	146
20–24	142
25–29	138
30–34	134
35–39	130
40–44	126
45–49	122
50–54	117
55–59	113
60–64	109

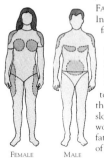

FAT DEPOSITS
In healthy people, fat deposits make up 16–25 per cent of body weight. As people get older, they often put on weight; they tend to be less active and their metabolism slows down. Men and women store excess fat in different parts of the body.

FEMALE   MALE

AVERAGE ENERGY REQUIREMENTS	
SEX: AGE OF SUBJECT	KJ/DAY
Infant: 9–12 months	4,200
Child: 8 years	8,770
Boy: 15 years	12,560
Girl: 15 years	9,560
Inactive woman	7,950
Active woman	9,000
Breast-feeding woman	11,250
Inactive man	10,460
Active man	12,560

BURNING ENERGY

Basketball
Male: 2,430 kJ per hour
Female: 2,080 kJ per hour

Judo
Male: 3,420 kJ per hour
Female: 2,950 kJ per hour

Panting helps take in more oxygen

Exercise produces heat

Running
Male: 3,400 kJ per hour
Female: 2,900 kJ per hour

BURNING KILOJOULES
Energy is measured in kilojoules (kJ) or kilocalories (kcal). If the energy you obtain from food is greater than the amount your body burns each day, you will put on weight.

CONVERSION KEY
4.2 kJ = 1 KCAL

NUTRITION AND DIET

FOR GOOD HEALTH, people need a regular supply of water and nutritious food. A balanced diet provides just the right amount of energy to fuel the muscles and bodily processes, such as tissue growth, breathing, and heartbeat. Many diseases are linked to poor diet. Eating too much fat, for example, can cause the arteries to clog up, leading to heart disease.

VITAL FOOD COMPONENTS

BALANCED DIET
Although most people obtain enough protein from their food, they tend not to eat enough starchy carbohydrates, fibre, vegetables, and fruit. Most people need to eat less fats and sugars. Multi-nutrient supplements containing vitamins and minerals are a popular way to correct imbalances.

VITAMINS
Found in fruit and vegetables, vitamins promote good health.

MINERALS
Also found in vegetables and fruit, minerals keep bones healthy.

FIBRE
The indigestible part of plant foods is fibre; it regulates bowel movements.

CARBOHYDRATES
In the form of starch and sugar, carbohydrates provide body cells with energy.

FATS AND OILS
Animal fats and plant oils keep nerves and other cells healthy and act as a fuel.

PROTEIN
Fish, meat, cheese, nuts, and beans contain protein, needed for growth and tissue repair.

VITAMINS AND MINERALS

TYPE	MAIN SOURCES	FUNCTIONS
VITAMIN A	Cod-liver and halibut oil; butter; milk; egg yolks; liver; fruit; carrots; green vegetables can be converted in the body into Vitamin A.	Helps tissue growth; maintains healthy eyes and skin; promotes the body's resistance to infection.
VITAMIN B COMPLEX/ FOLIC ACID	Meat; kidneys; yeast extract; fortified cereals; bread; sprouts; cauliflower	Maintains a healthy nervous system, digestion, and metabolism; helps enzymes and hormones to function; produces energy; keeps skin and hair healthy.
VITAMIN C	Fresh vegetables; fruit, especially citrus fruit; (Vitamin C can be lost through cooking.)	Keeps skin, teeth, gums, bones, blood vessels, and tissues healthy; improves iron absorption; aids the immune system and heals wounds.
VITAMIN D	Oily fish; cod-liver oil; egg yolks; margarine; whole (fortified) milk; manufactured in skin on exposure to sunlight.	Vital for the absorption of calcium and phosphate from the intestines; calcium is vital for strong bones and teeth.
VITAMIN E	Wheat germ; oil; avocado pear; nuts; margarine; butter; eggs; wholemeal cereals; seeds; nuts; fish; meat; green leafy vegetables	Preserves body fats; helps in the formation of red blood cells; maintains healthy cell membranes.
IRON (MINERAL)	Red meat; kidneys; bread; beans; flour; egg yolk; dried fruit; curry powder; nuts; some vegetables	Essential for the production of the red blood pigment, haemoglobin; fortifies muscles; fights infection.
CALCIUM (MINERAL)	Dairy products; fish; tinned sardines; bread; green vegetables	Maintains healthy bones and teeth; aids muscle contraction; helps conduct nerve signals; assists blood clotting.

HUMAN BODY TIMELINE

THE STUDY OF THE HUMAN BODY fascinated the ancient world, but from about AD 300, for over 1,000 years, the Christian church discouraged research in Europe. Advances were confined to Asia and Arabia, until the Renaissance gave rise to a new spirit of enquiry.

C.28,000 BC   C.100 BC

C.8,000 BC–C.2,000 BC

• c.28,000 BC Prehistoric sculptures and cave paintings depict the shape of the human body.

• c.6,500 BC Trepanning practised – making holes in the skull is perhaps a form of early surgery.

• 2,300 BC *Nei Ching* (Medicine of the Yellow Emperor) is written in China. It includes a description of the circulation of the blood.

TREPANNED SKULL, C. 6,500 BC

• c.3,000–1,600 BC Egyptians develop interest in anatomy. They believe the heart is the centre of thought and the soul.

• c.2,000 BC Early methods of birth control show some knowledge of human biology;

C.1,000 BC–C.300 BC

sheaths stop sperm from entering a woman's body.

• c.1,000 BC Surgery practised in India, including amputations, skin grafts, and the removal of cataracts.

• c.400 BC Hippocrates (c.460–377 BC), the most celebrated physician of ancient times, describes diseases and their cures. He also draws up the Hippocratic oath – a code of practice for doctors.

• c.384–322 BC Aristotle of Greece makes the first recorded attempts to study anatomy, but he does not dissect a human body.

• c.335–280 BC Herophilus

HIPPOCRATES C.400 BC

C.300 BC–C.100 BC

dissects bodies and claims the brain is the centre of the nervous system.

• c.300 BC Egyptian Erasistratus (310–250 BC) makes many discoveries: the function of the epiglottis in the larynx; the tricuspid heart valve; motor and sensory nerves; and how muscles shorten to pull bones. Incorrectly believes arteries contain air.

• c.300 BC Chinese physician Hua T'o pioneers the use of anaesthesia and performs abdominal surgery.

• c.100 BC Roman physicians practise Caesarian section, a surgical operation to deliver a baby through the mother's abdomen. (A practice still popular today.)

AD 170   1691

c.170–c.1590	1615–1665	1672–1691

- c.170 The Greek physician Claudius Galen (129–199) writes *On the Use of the Parts of the Human Body*. He observes that arteries contain blood, not air. Incorrectly asserts that four humours (fluids) circulate through the body to determine a person's well-being. (This is widely believed for the next 1400 years.)

- 1000 Arabian anatomist Avicenna's *Canon of Medicine* is published – his information derives from dissected human bodies.

- c.1450 Invention of the printing press spreads knowledge and coincides with the Renaissance, a period of renewed scientific enquiry.

- 1543 Using stolen corpses as his models, Belgian Andreas Vesalius (1514–64) draws the first accurate anatomical drawings in *De Humani Corporis Fabrica* ("On the Fabric of the Human Body").

DRAWING BY VESALIUS, 1543

- c.1590 Dutch spectacle-maker Hans Jenssen

invents the compound microscope.

- 1615 Italian physician Sanctorius (1561–1636) invents the thermometer, the first accurate method of measuring body temperature.

- 1628 William Harvey (1578–1657), physician to King James I and Charles I of England, describes the circulation of the blood.

BLOOD CIRCULATION, 1628

- 1658 Dutch anatomist Jan Swammerdam (1637–80) uses a microscope to observe red blood cells.

- 1660s Italian microscopist Marcello Malpighi (1628–94) discovers filtering units in the kidneys and the bronchial tree in the lungs.

- 1664 Danish microscopist Niels Stensen (1638–86) recognizes that muscles are made up of bundles of fibres.

- 1665 Physicist Robert Hooke (1635–1703) coins the word "cell" in his book

Micrographia, after studying the structure of a piece of cork under a homemade microscope

- 1672 Dutch physician Regnier de Graaf (1641–73) describes the female reproductive system in detail for the first time.

- c.1675 English chemist, John Mayhow's (1640–79) chemical investigations on breathing show that a vital ingredient in air supports life. (Later French scientist, A.L. Lavoisier (1743–94) identifies this ingredient as oxygen.)

- 1677 Dutch biologist Anton Leeuwenhoek (1632–1723) identifies male sperm cells.

- 1691 English physician Clopton Havers (1650–1701) observes the complex structure of compact bone.

MICROSCOPE, 1660s

1791   1898

1791–1818

• 1791 Italian anatomist Luigi Galvani (1737–98) discovers that electricity can be produced by chemicals in the body. He touches the legs of a dead frog with two different metals and they twitch.

• 1796 English physician Edward Jenner (1749–1823) discovers the principles of vaccination and immunity. He protects a boy against smallpox by immunizing him with a mild cowpox virus.

• 1800 Italian physicist Alessandro Volta (1745–1827) describes the effects of electricity on muscles.

• 1801 English physiologist Thomas Young (1773–1829) suggests that the eye sees colours – red, blue, and yellow – by responding to three different wavelengths.

• 1816 French doctor René Laënnec (1781–1826) uses the first stethoscope – a rolled-up newspaper – to listen to a patient's heart.

• 1818 The first blood transfusion is carried out by

STETHOSCOPE, C.1820

1844–1865

Dr James Blundell. (Since the four blood groups are not discovered until 1910, it is not very successful.)

• 1844 Laughing gas (nitrous oxide) is used as an anaesthetic during the extraction of a tooth by an American dentist, H. Wells.

• 1846 American dentist William Morton (1819–68) pioneers ether as a general anaesthetic.

• 1851 The ophthalmoscope is invented in Germany to examine the back of the eyes.

• 1853 The first hypodermic syringe is used to give an injection under the skin.

CARBOLIC STEAM SPRAY, 1860

• 1860 English surgeon Joseph Lister (1827–1912) uses antiseptic (weak carbolic acid) to prevent infection during operations.

• 1865 French chemist Louis Pasteur (1822–95) invents "pasturization" to heat-treat

1880–1898

EARLY SPHYGMOMANOMETER, 1883

food, killing off bacteria. He shows how bacteria spreads disease.

• 1880 Czech Samuel Von Basch (1837–1905) invents the sphygmomanometer, the first instrument for measuring blood pressure.

• c.1885 German Rudolf Virchow (1821–1902) recognizes cells make up all body tissues and that many diseases are caused by changes in the cells.

• 1895 German physicist Wilhelm Röentgen (1845–1923) discovers X-rays. First pictures feature his wife's hand.

• 1895 Austrian doctor Sigmund Freud (1856–1939) studies the unconscious mind and establishes a method to treat mental illness: psychoanalysis.

• 1898 Italian professor Camillio Golgi (1844–1926) stains cells and shows how certain membranes are stacked together to form an organelle (a Golgi body).

• 1905 British researchers coin the word "hormone" from the Greek word

1905

1990s

1905–1950s

for "to stir up".

• 1910 Austrian pathologist Dr Karl Landsteiner (1868–1943) discovers the four blood groups: A, B, AB, O.

• 1912 British biochemist Sir Frederick Gowland Hopkins (1861–1947) discovers vitamins.

• 1918 The first brain X-ray is taken.

• 1920 The first EEG machine is developed to record electrical brainwaves.

• 1931 German physicist Ernst Ruska (1906–88) wins the Nobel prize for inventing the electron microscope.

• 1950 The first kidney transplant is performed by a Dr Lawler in Chicago, USA.

• 1950s Birth-control pill is developed. In general use by the 1960s.

• 1952 Jonas Salk produces a vaccine against polio. (Mass vaccination begins in the mid-1950s.)

• 1953 American biologist James Watson (b. 1928) and English biochemist Francis Crick (b. 1916) discover

1952–1973

that genetic material (DNA) has a double helix (spiral) structure, enabling genes to pass from one generation to another.

• 1953 American surgeon John Gibbon (1903–74) develops the heart–lung machine to pump a patient's blood during open-heart surgery.

DNA, 1953

• 1954 The first internal heart pacemaker is fitted in Stockholm, Sweden.

• 1958 The endoscope, a telescope that looks inside the body, is developed in the USA.

• 1967 South African surgeon Christiaan Barnard (b. 1922) performs the first heart transplant. The patient lives for 18 days.

CT SCAN, 1973

• 1973 CT (Computerized Tomography) scan produces a more detailed picture of

1970s–1990s

the internal organs than an X-ray.

• 1970s NMR (Nuclear Magnetic Resonance) scan uses radio waves to produce detailed images of the body's insides.

BIONIC ARM, 1976

• 1976 An electronically operated (bionic) arm is fitted to a road accident victim in Australia.

• 1978 The first test-tube baby, Louise Brown, is born in Britain.

• 1981 The first heart and lung transplant is performed in California.

• 1984 US geneticist John Sanford develops a gene gun, which fires genetic material into a cell at high speed, to alter its structure.

• 1980s–1990s Microsurgery uses advanced technology: fibre-optic endoscopes and lasers.

• 1990s Virtual reality is used to study the body in three-dimensions, and in the field of genetics discoveries are made regularly. The human genetic code is now being mapped.

Glossary

ABDUCTION
Movement of a body part away from the midline (body axis).

ABSCESS
A collection of pus cells usually triggered by an infection.

ADDUCTION
Movement of a body part towards the midline.

ALVEOLI
Tiny air sacs in the lungs.

ANTIBODIES
Proteins, in the blood and other body fluids, that fight infection.

ARTERIOLE
Small artery.

ARTERY
A thick-walled vessel that carries blood away from the heart.

ARTHRITIS
Inflammation of a joint.

ATRIA
The two upper chambers of the heart.

AXON
Fine filament that carries impulses away from a nerve cell body.

BOLUS
A lump of swallowed food.

BLASTOCYST
A ball of cells containing a fluid-filled cavity formed from a fertilized egg.

BRONCHIOLE
A small airway in the lung.

CAPILLARIES
Narrow blood vessels that form a network throughout the body.

CARTILAGE
A tough tissue, associated with bone, that protects joints.

CEREBROSPINAL FLUID
A nourishing and cushioning fluid that surrounds the brain and spinal cord.

CHROMOSOME
One of 46 collections of genes found in a cell nucleus.

CHYME
Semi-digested food found in the stomach.

CILIA
A tiny hair-like projection from a cell

wall, which may have a beating action.

CNS
Central nervous system (brain and spinal cord).

COLLAGEN
A structural protein found in most body tissues.

CORNEA
Transparent layer that protects the front of the eye.

CORTEX
Firm, outer part of some organs, glands, hairs, and bones.

CRANIAL NERVES
Twelve pairs of nerves that are connected directly to the brain.

DENDRITE
Fine projections branching off from a neuron body that receive impulses from neighbouring neurons.

DENTINE
Tough layer of tooth beneath the enamel. See ENAMEL. See NEURON.

DERMIS
Inner layer of skin.

DIAPHRAGM
A large, flat muscle that separates the chest and abdominal cavities.

DIASTOLE
Resting phase of the heartbeat.

DNA
Deoxyribonucleic acid – genetic material found in the cell nucleus.

ECG
Electrocardiogram – tracing of electrical activity in the heart.

EEG
Electroencephalogram – tracing of electrical activity in the brain.

EMBRYO
The first 8 weeks of life inside the womb when tiny organs are being formed.

ENAMEL
Tooth coating; it is the hardest substance in the body.

ENDOCRINE GLAND
A gland that secretes hormones directly into the bloodstream.

ENZYME
A protein that speeds up a chemical reaction.

EPIDERMIS
The outer layer of skin.

EPIGLOTTIS
Cartilage flap at top of trachea that prevents food from going down "the wrong way".

EXOCRINE GLAND
A gland that secretes its products through a duct into a body cavity or onto the body surface.

EXTENSION
Straightening of a joint, so that the angle between two bones becomes greater.

FAECES
Semi-solid waste products of digestion.

FETUS
The stage of human development, from about 8 weeks after fertilization until birth, marked by rapid growth.

FIBRIN
Protein involved in blood clotting and wound healing.

FLEXION
Bending of a joint, so that the angle between two bones becomes smaller.

GENES
A unit of hereditary information, made up of DNA, that contains enough information to make a specific protein.

GLAND
See ENDOCRINE AND EXOCRINE GLANDS.

GLIAL CELLS
Cells that support and nourish neurons. See NEURON.

GREY MATTER
The part of the brain and spinal cord that contains neuron cell bodies. See NEURON.

GUT
The intestines.

HAEMOGLOBIN
Red blood pigment that carries oxygen to the tissues.

HEPATOCYTES
Liver cells.

HORMONES
Chemical messengers released from an endocrine gland directly into the bloodstream to trigger an action elsewhere in the body.

KERATIN
A tough, protective protein found in the skin, hair, and nails.

LACTEAL
Small lymph vessel found in intestinal villi. See VILLI.

LIGAMENTS
Strong, fibrous tissues that bind joints.

LYMPH
A fluid that drains from body tissues into lymph vessels – unlike blood, it contains only one type of cell, lymphocytes. See LYMPHOCYTES.

LYMPH NODES
Swellings in the lymph system where lymphocytes are stored and through which lymphatic fluid is filtered from infection.

LYMPHOCYTES
Small white blood cells that are involved in antibody production. See ANTIBODIES.

MARROW
The soft inner part of long bones, where blood cells are made.

MEDULLA
Soft, internal portion of some glands, organs, hair, and bones.

MEMBRANE
A thin lining or covering layer.

MENINGES
Three membranes that surround the brain and the spinal cord.

MITOCHONDRION
Small structure found inside cells where energy-producing chemical reactions take place.

MORULA
Ball of cells formed when a fertilized egg starts to divide.

MOTOR NERVES
Nerves that carry signals from the central nervous system to the muscles.

MYOFIBRE
Bundles of cells found in muscle fibre.

MYOFIBRIL
Muscle-building blocks made up of two proteins, myosin and actin.

NEPHRON
Filtration unit found in the kidneys.

NEURON
Nerve cell that can carry electrical impulses.

NUCLEUS
The central control region of the cell.

OESOPHAGUS
Tube that leads from the mouth to the stomach.

ORGANELLE
One of many tiny structures found inside body cells.

OSTEON
Small unit used to build up compact bone.

PERISTALSIS
Process by which food is propelled through the digestive tract by waves of muscular contraction.

PHAGOCYTOSIS
Process by which some white blood cells engulf and destroy invading organisms, such as bacteria or a virus.

PINNA
Ear flap.

PITUITARY GLAND
The most important endocrine gland, which is situated at the base of the brain.

PLASMA
The fluid and dissolved substances in which blood cells float.

PLATELETS
Cell fragments involved in blood clotting.

PLEURAL MEMBRANE
Sheet of tissue lining the inner surface of the chest cavity and the lung's outer surface.

PULMONARY
Relating to the lungs, such as the pulmonary circulation.

PUPIL
An opening in the centre of the iris, through which light passes to reach the retina. See RETINA.

RECEPTORS
Specialized structures that detect stimuli and trigger signals that produce a particular response in a body part.

RED BLOOD CELLS
Cells circulating in the bloodstream that contain haemoglobin. See HAEMOGLOBIN.

RETINA
Light-sensitive lining at the rear of the eye.

SALIVA
A digestive fluid secreted by the salivary glands in the mouth.

SCLERA
Tough, outer white of the eye.

SENSORY NERVES
Nerves that carry information from various body receptors back to the central nervous system. See RECEPTORS.

SEPTUM
A dividing wall, such as the nasal septum.

SINUSOIDS
Blood-filled spaces found in some tissues, such as in the liver.

SUPERIOR VENA CAVA
The largest vein in the body.

SUTURES
Special joints that lock skull bones together so that they cannot move.

SYNAPSE
Small gap at the junction between two neurons. See NEURON.

SYSTOLE
Contraction stage of the heartbeat.

TENDON
Strong connective tissue that attaches muscle to bone.

THYMUS
A gland that makes and stores T-lymphocytes in childhood. It almost disappears by adulthood.

TISSUE
A collection of cells or fibres that perform a similar function.

TRABECULAE
Small bony struts that make up spongy (cancellous) bone.

TYMPANUM
Eardrum.

VALVES
Flaps of tissue that prevent the backflow of blood in large veins and in the heart.

VEIN
A thin-walled vessel that carries blood back to the heart.

VENTRICLES
The two lower chambers of the heart.

VENULE
Small vein.

VILLI
Small projections in the intestinal wall that absorb nutrients.

WHITE BLOOD CELLS
A variety of colourless blood cells, such as neutrophils and lymphocytes, that protect the body from invading organisms. See LYMPHOCYTES.

WHITE MATTER
The part of the brain and spinal cord that contains neuron axons. See AXON.

ZONA PELLUCIDA
The tough, outer membrane or "shell" of a human egg.

ZYGOTE
A newly fertilized egg.

Index

Acknowledgements

Dorling Kindersley would like to thank:
Hilary Bird for the index; Louise Cox
and Andrea Jeffrey-Hall for design
assistance; Caroline Potts for picture
research.

Illustrations by:
Joanna Cameron, Mike Courtney, William
Donohue, Simone End, Guiliano Fornani,
Mike Gillah, Nick Hall, Sandie Hill, Dave
Hopkins, Janos Marffy, Kate Miller, Colin
Salmon, Michael Saunders, Clive Spong,
John Temperton, Lydia Umney, Peter
Visscher, John Woodcock, Dan Wright.

Photographs by:
Geoff Dann, Philip Dowell, Dave King,
Dave Rudkin, Jane Stockman.

Picture Credits
The publisher would like to thank the
following for their kind permission to
reproduce their photographs:

t=top c=centre a=above b=below l=left
r=right.

Allsport: Mike Powell 112l; Lester
Cheeseman: 108 tr; Donkin Models:
16–17c; Gorden Models: 58c; Natural
History Museum: 13bc, 13br, 18–19,
20–21, 24–25; Queen Mary's University
Hospital: 119br; Rex Features Ltd: Sipa
39bl; Science Museum: 117br, 118tr,
118–119b; Science Photo Library: 17c,
31tl, 40–41, Michael Abbey 34bl, CNRI
10–11, 17tc, 80–81, 89bl, 91br, Secchi-
Leaque/Roussel-UCLAF / CNRI 17ca, 97cr,
Prof C Ferlaud/CNRI 76c, 76cr, Manfed
Kage 60–61, David Leah 106tr, Dr P Marazzi
68l, Prof P Motta/Dept of Anatomy,
University "La Sapienza", Rome 22bl, 87tl,
100br, NIBSC 71cr, OMIKRON 54tr,
David Parker 72l, Petite Format/Nestlè
103tl, D Phillips 94–95, 101tl, Dr Clive
Rocher 79cr, Dept of Clinical Radiology,
Salisbury District Hospital 30bl, David
Scharf 38tl, 66tr, Dr K F R Schiller 87b,
Western Opthalmic Hospital 109tl; Sporting
Pictures (UK) Ltd: 37tl.

Every effort has been made to trace the
copyright holders and we apologize in
advance for any unintentional omissions. We
would be pleased to insert the appropriate
acknowledgement in any subsequent edition
of this publication.